The Commandant's Last Ride

Enjoy the book;
Enjoy the town!
Best wishes

Published by
Ten-Digit Press
1025 W. Cape Rock Drive
Cape Girardeau, MO 63701-2706
mlevans@brick.net

Printed in the United States of America

To all those who encouraged my writing during my childhood and youth: my mom, many North St. Francois County teachers — especially Dorothy Moore, Mary Wilfong, Cynthia Elder and Elaine Johnson, my cousin Peggy Van Ostran Boyd, my friends at school who patiently read my countless short stories and novels and to the late Professor Mary Ellen Forderhase at Central Methodist College.

Also to all those who have encouraged my writing and research since becoming acquainted with Ste. Genevieve and who share my love of old buildings.

The Commandant's Last Ride

Mark L. Evans

Contents

Foreword

Ste. Genevieve is an extraordinary national treasure. It preserves in its buildings and its streets, in its cultural and natural landscapes, a material record of an important and fascinating aspect of our national history. And, it does so to an extent matched by few other places. Its significance is quickly understood and deeply felt, as was so apparent from the national—even international—response when the town was seriously threatened during the terrible flood of 1993.

The French colonial empire in North America as it developed in the seventeenth and eighteenth centuries stretched from the eastern settlements in Canada, through the Great Lakes, down the Mississippi valley, to islands in the Caribbean. Intrepid *voyageurs* established routes for the fur trade as far west as the Rocky Mountains, long before Lewis and Clark explored the same territory for the United States government. Its settled western frontier consisted of a group of villages—including Ste. Genevieve—in the middle Mississippi valley which date from the eighteenth century, in an area that had seen a major center of urbanized Native American culture centuries earlier.

The first of these villages were on the eastern bank of the Mississippi—Cahokia in 1699, Kaskaskia in 1703, and Fort de Chartres in 1719 being the most important. French settlers were soon crossing the river, to mine lead in the hills to the west of where Ste. Genevieve would develop, to make salt at the Saline River a few miles south of Ste. Genevieve, and to farm the rich bottom land of the large common field just south of the present town. By the middle of the eighteenth century people began to build houses along the river near their farm plots so as not to have to cross the river every day. This became the first of Ste. Genevieve, and a census in 1752 makes clear that a small village was in place by that date.

With the treaty of Paris in 1763 ending the French and Indian War, the Mississippi River became an international boundary, separating the English territory on the east from the Spanish territory on the west. The French settlers, seeing their prospects more favorable under a Catholic

Bourbon king than under an English Protestant king, began to leave their homes on the east side of the river for Ste. Genevieve and the new village of St. Louis. Ste. Genevieve grew rapidly, reaching a population of 691 in the census of 1772.

The river then as well as now was a threat to Ste. Genevieve, especially for the village stretching along a riverbank that regularly eroded. A major flood in 1785 led to the decision to relocate the town to the slightly higher ground of the *petite côtes*, between the two branches of Gabouri creek, north of the original village. A decade later this process was complete. It is this settlement, with its neat grid plan quite different from the more linear original village, that we know today.

The older settlements on what became the Illinois side of the river preserve a few interesting buildings, in Cahokia especially and the reconstructed Fort de Chartres. But what had been the largest community, Kaskaskia, was almost entirely lost when the Mississippi changes its course toward the end of the nineteenth century. St. Louis preserved extensive elements of its French past until the first half of the twentieth century but finally even the street pattern was erased, save a small segment in what is today called Laclede's Landing. Ironically, it was the development of the Jefferson National Expansion Memorial national park with a mission to commemorate the role of St. Louis in the development of the West, that led to the obliteration of the French street pattern and even to the regrading of the natural topography that had been one of the features that attracted Pierre Laclede to the site. But Ste. Genevieve, spared the destructive forces of both nature and modern development, comes down to us with a strong, tangible presence of its early founding.

The historical importance of Ste. Genevieve began to be understood more widely in the early twentieth century thanks to the work of pioneer historians, and with that came an appreciation for its early buildings. This appreciation developed an aesthetic aspect as well, as people began to see these quaint old buildings as charming and attractive, even beautiful—something that was happening in other parts of the country, too, at this time. Good evidence for this is the founding of the Ste. Genevieve Artists Colony in 1932. This summer colony brought in artists from many places, especially St. Louis, until the Second World War. They found their subject matter in this quaint old town and its inhabitants.

Historical studies of Ste. Genevieve took a serious architectural direction in the 1930s. The Historic American Buildings Survey sent a team of architects to make measured, architectural drawings of the early buildings, and professional photographers to take pictures of them. Charles Peterson, an architect with the National Park Service in St. Louis who had been responsible for the creation of the Historic American Buildings Survey in 1933, began an extensive study of the French building traditions in the mid-Mississippi valley as background for the development of the national park in St. Louis. This resulted in his pioneering publications on the subject, about Ste. Genevieve in 1941 and St. Louis in 1947.

Charles van Ravenswaay, as director of the project to prepare the WPA guide to Missouri in the 1930s, took a special interest in Ste. Genevieve, an interest he continued after the Second World War when he became director of the Missouri Historical Society in St. Louis. Van Ravenswaay and Peterson, with these shared interests, became friends, and in the 1950s recommended a young architect on the faculty of Washington University, Ernest Connally, to the Mathews family and the Colonial Dames to direct the restoration of the Bolduc house, a landmark restoration project in this country. A decade later, Connally went to Washington as Associate Director of the National Park Service to organize the new office of Archaeology and Historic Preservation which has become the most important public agency for historic preservation in America.

It wasn't just outsiders who were finding Ste. Genevieve of great interest, but a growing core of the local community did as well, and joined in the efforts to study and preserve the architecture of their community. Being residents and there every day, they gave a new and vital life to preservation. Of the many who participated, Lucille Basler stands out especially. Using her experience in a title guarantee business, she began detailed studies of the ownership of individual buildings—eventually dozens of them—the first systematic preservation survey of Ste. Genevieve. She received an award from the National Trust for Historic Preservation for this work. She played the key role in the creation of the local preservation organization, the Foundation for the Restoration of Ste. Genevieve, and served as the first Chair of the Landmarks Commission. Others began to take on the responsibility of owning historic buildings, even restoring them and opening them to the public, no one more memorably than Frankye and Boats Donze.

The pioneers in the preservation movement have many followers today, both local people and others who have moved to Ste. Genevieve to take on the responsibilities of stewardship for historic buildings that they have purchased. And those early historians and architectural historians have their present followers—quite a community of them—whose work enlarges our knowledge and understanding of this national treasure.

In Ste. Genevieve we find the largest concentration in all of North America of buildings of the French tradition in their historic setting. Overlaying it are the contributions of the Anglo Americans and the Germans who followed the French. It is a cultural landscape of great texture and immense richness. This guide to it by Mark Evans, very well informed and engagingly written, is welcome indeed. Ste. Genevieve attracts a growing number of visitors every year, and his walking tour will help them to experience the history embodied in this place.

If you are the visitor, play his words off against what you see. Walk through these buildings, notice their plan arrangements and imagine them at use, both when they were new and over time. See yourself in them, not just now but back then. Remember what you learned at one when you go to another—seeing them in relation to each other, they start to suggest answers to other questions about life in this community and its social structure. Pay attention to the materials of which the houses are made, how they are put together, how they are finished and decorated, how the daily problems of shelter are solved. The builder' s traditions here are distinctive, of a high standard, and quite different between the French, the Anglo American, and the German. Though these building traditions are different, the buildings are all pretty much of the same size and scale, so that the feel of the town that we get from walking around it is very much that of the original. So, notice the larger urban patterns, the relation of the buildings to each other, their relation to the streets, and how they and the landscaping features shape the open spaces.

With this book in hand, a rich historical treat is in store for you as you walk through Ste. Genevieve.

Osmund Overby

Introduction

I didn't feel like sitting through a concert on this particular late May evening. The St. Louis musicians, helping bridge the gap between the end of the Festival la Nouvelle France and the quarterly Foundation for Restoration of Ste. Genevieve meeting that night, were top quality. In the sticky Missouri evening air, though, sitting in a suit and tie and listening to strangers perform was not for me. I slipped out, got out of my suit jacket and drove downtown.

I am thankful now that I *did* skip out of the concert. The twenty minutes or so that I spent alone with Ste. Genevieve that evening helped cement my conviction that this book needed to be done. Getting a can of soda, I strolled Merchant Street, from South Main to Second Street, taking in the fine old features of the Felix Vallé House, the Mammy Shaw House, the Dufour Stone Building and others. I was virtually alone downtown. Once again, Ste. Genevieve connected with me.

No doubt author Gregory M. Franzwa, whose imminently important work, *The Story of Old Ste. Genevieve,* this book will probably never rival in importance or longevity, made such a connection in the late 1960s. He has described staying at the hotel during a convention and taking a moonlit midnight walk. The old town reached out and connected with him that night. It has done so with numerous visitors and residents over the years.

A handful of people of various ages have questioned why anyone would want to write about Ste. Genevieve. It's too small, too cliquish, too boring, they have said. To me this seems like missing the forest for the trees. Ste. Genevieve is not Williamsburg; it is not Branson; it is not Boston. It will never be any of those places; yet it doesn't *need* to be any of those places. Perhaps Ste. Genevieve is an acquired taste for some. For a great many weary souls, though, the old French town is a special haven.

Trying to put into words just what makes Ste. Genevieve special is difficult. Trying to convince on-line chat room friends to hold a live get together there proved difficult. The one Internet friend who did visit, though, was immediately a stronger Ste. Genevieve supporter than I. For many of us, it simply clicks. It connects with us at some deep, subconscious level. For me, the connection was almost immediate. Then, after working at the *Ste. Genevieve Herald* for several months, I discovered that my great-great-great-great-great grandfather (Antoine Aubuchon) had been a town founder. This, naturally, cemented the bond. I was returning to my ancestral home without even realizing it.

Even for those with no genealogical ties to Ste. Genevieve, though, the town still reaches out and connects. On this late May evening I could feel it. Describing it is still a difficult proposition. Words like "quiet," "serene," "historic," or even "quaint" or "rustic" only touch on one or two aspects of Ste. Genevieve. No doubt the French have some phrase to describe it. Whatever this special charm may be, I hope the readers of this book make that connection. Walk the streets, relax, visit the shops and take the tours, check out the historic architecture. Mainly, though, just let down your guard and give the town a chance to connect. Once it does, you'll be a believer.

Mark L. Evans
Cape Girardeau, MO
June 8, 2001

Acknowledgements

In working on two Ste. Genevieve book projects, I have found people nothing less than gracious in sharing information, making helpful pointers and offering encouragement. Those who have trod the publishing path before me have been especially helpful. Gregory M. Franzwa, whose *The Story of Old Ste. Genevieve*, has introduced two generations to the old town, has always been encouraging and ready with constructive criticism or advice. So, too, has Dr. Carl J. Ekberg, the leading scholar on colonial Ste. Genevieve and probably the leading living scholar on the French and Spanish empire in the Upper Mississippi Valley.

Both were very generous in helping my partner Bill Naeger and I when we undertook our coffee table book, *Ste. Genevieve: A Leisurely Stroll Through History,* in 1997. The paths were made easier for us by those who had blazed them before us. Likewise, Bill has joined the others in encouraging me on this project. In getting my feet wet, working in the field of Ste. Genevieve history, other huge figures have been helpful over the years, as well. The legendary Charles E. Peterson, founder of the Historic American Buildings Survey and the man who in many ways put Ste. Genevieve on the map, has always been quick to return correspondence and answer questions, as has Dr. Charles Belesi, another French colonial expert and author.

Of course special thanks and appreciation has to go to the author of this work's foreword, Dr. Osmund Overby. Not only does his foreword lend this book an air of respectability, his earlier work supplies the bulk of its information. Although I have had two historic preservation classes in graduate school, I am no architect. The foundation of the building vignettes in this book is the Historic American Buildings Survey of the 1980s, which Dr. Overby headed. Anyone comparing a copy of the HABS report to the text of this book will immediately see that most of the architectural details come from it. Fellow University of Missouri professor, Dr. Richard Guyette, has also been most helpful in sharing his knowledge of dendrochronology. It was exciting actually getting to see Dr. Guyette take a tree ring sample in the spring of 2001.

Thanks go to the staffs of The Missouri Historical Society and its staff, including photo archivists Duane Sneddeker and Ellen Thomason and The State Historical Society of Missouri and its staff, including Christine Montgomery and Kerry Nichols. Their help and the information and photographs obtained from these organizations have been most valuable.

So have the photographs borrowed from local collections. (See the photo credit page for details.)

Locally, plenty of individuals and organizations have been most helpful. Tim Conley, owner and restorer of The Old Louisiana Academy, has been one of my strongest supporters in undertaking various historical writing projects. In fact, it was his suggestion that I consider writing the series of articles for the *Herald* that looked at the controversies over the historic building dates in town. That series, more than anything else, launched my historic writing career – if two books can be called a career!

My former boss, Jean Feld Rissover, has encouraged me not only in this particular project, but in my career in general. She saw a greater potential in a thirty-six-year-old journalist than covering high school sports and local news and urged me to resume my education and aim for a more fulfilling career. I will always appreciate her belief in me.

Jim Baker, site director of the Missouri Department of Natural Resources' historic sites in town, as well as Ellie Douglas, Bill Miller and the rest of the DNR staff, have been most helpful whenever any information has been needed. They and artist Lewis Pruneau have also been most generous in allowing me to photograph Pruneau's magnificent diorama of Ste. Genevieve in 1832. Allowing me to reproduce some of these in this book was also most gracious of them. The diorama is a must-see for anyone visiting Ste. Genevieve.

Community leaders in the Ste. Genevieve Chamber of Commerce, the new Ste. Genevieve Convention & Visitors Bureau, the French Colonial Merchants Association, The Foundation for Restoration of Ste. Genevieve, Inc., and various bed and breakfast owners and local merchants have all been quite encouraging and helpful. I also appreciate the Foundation allowing me to reproduce the 1938 Bernard Peters painting of Jean Baptiste Vallé, now in its possession. The National Society of Colonial Dames in The State of Missouri has also been most gracious and helpful.

Special thanks goes to Anne Herzog, a Ste. Genevieve native who was bitten by the same historic preservation bug that has infected many of us. A historic preservation major at Southeast Missouri State University in Cape Girardeau at this writing, she made calls on many local businesses and groups, trying to secure sponsorships for this publication.

Thanks also goes to Kim Hawley, Jullie Huffmon and others at Walsworth Publishing, who put up with numerous bid requests, changes in book size and other waffling on my part. Walsworth has been very easy to work with during this process.

To all these and any others whom I may have inevitably left out, I offer my grateful thanks. I hope each one enjoys this book.

Mark L. Evans
June 8, 2001

Terminology

For the reader to get the most out of this book, the following terms and acronyms should be understood.

Creole – This term refers merely to anyone of European ancestry who was born in North America. In the Upper Mississippi Valley, most of the French Creoles migrated from Canada. The term Creole, if used properly – as it was in the colonial period – has nothing to do with mixed race. A separate term, "mulatto," refers to children born to European and black or European and Indian parents.

HABS – The Historic American Buildings Survey was the brainchild of Charles E. Peterson. Launched as part of the New Deal in 1933, it put 1,000 out of work architects to work, drawing and recording information on historic buildings across the nation. Professional photographers, as Dr. Overby notes in his foreword, were also hired to take large format photos. Peterson himself handled much of the Ste. Genevieve HABS work during the 1930s. Later, in the 1980s, Overby led a University of Missouri-Columbia group that conducted an updated HABS survey of some 1,200 structures in Ste. Genevieve. These reports, which are in the public domain, form the basis of most of the building information in this book.

Dendrochronology – This is tree ring dating, a science developed in the early twentieth century in the American Southwest. Dr. Richard Guyette of the University of Missouri-Columbia, performed the first tree ring tests on a house in Missouri, when he tested the Bequette-Ribault House in Ste. Genevieve in 1984. He tested twenty-four Ste. Genevieve buildings during the mid 1980s and has been privately hired to test many more in the subsequent years. The Department of Interior accepts dendrochronology as the final word in dating a building.

French building terms – French Creoles in the Louisiana Territory had two primary building styles. They were *poteaux en terre* ("posts-in-the-ground"), and *poteaux sur solle* ("posts-on-a-sill"). Both were used with vertical logs. *Poteaux en terre* logs were sharpened on the end and sat in a trench, which was then backfilled. Mixtures of *bouzillage* (a mixture of straw, clay, grass and basically anything else at hand – such as animal hair) or *pierrotage* (a stone and lime mortar mix) were infilled between the massive vertical logs – usually spaced about six inches apart. They were then covered with whitewash in most cases. In *Poteaux sur solle* construction, large wooden beams were set on a stone foundation and used as sills.

Le Grand Champ **–** French for "The Big Field," this was and still is where Ste. Genevieve farmers raised their crops. The food basket of most of the Louisiana Territory, Ste. Genevieve managed tremendous agricultural production over the years, despite frequent flooding. Pecan and walnut trees were planted in straight lines to mark property lines in the field. Also known as the "The Common Field" or "The Big Commons," the land was not communally owned. Each farmer was granted farm land, based on ability to farm it, wealth, social standing, etc. A common fence around the agricultural field, though, *was* maintained by the entire community.

For a greater understanding of daily life in colonial Ste. Genevieve, Carl J. Ekberg's *Colonial Ste. Genevieve: An Adventure on the Mississippi Frontier* is highly recommended, as is the out-of-print *A Glossary of Mississippi Valley French, 1673-1850,* by John Francis McDermott. Gregory M. Franzwa's charming book, *The Story of Old Ste. Genevieve,* is also a must.

Pictorial Glossary

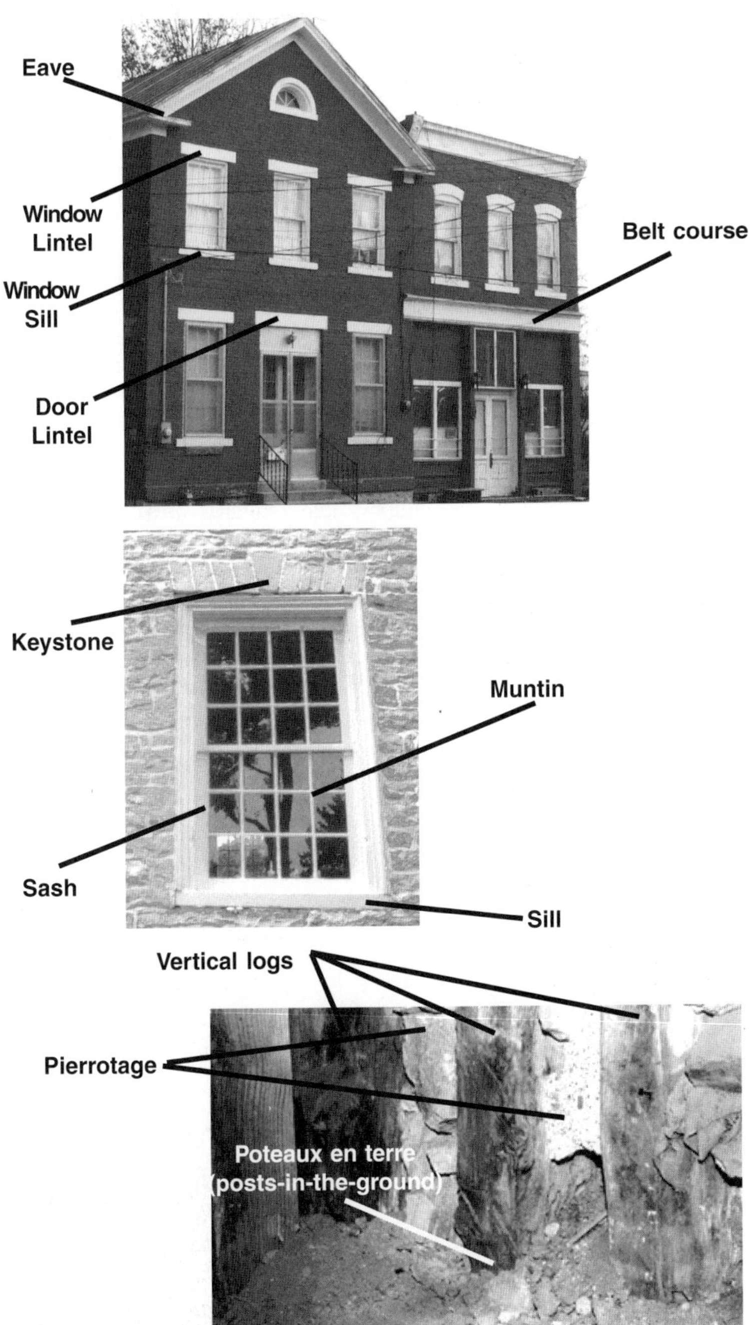
Eave
Window
Lintel
Window
Sill
Door
Lintel
Belt course
Keystone
Muntin
Sash
Sill
Vertical logs
Pierrotage
Poteaux en terre
(posts-in-the-ground)

The Commandant's Last Ride

Wednesday, August 1, 1849

The dark gray clouds swirling among the light, cottony clouds hinted that more thunderstorms and rain might well sweep the Mississippi River Valley again by evening. Still, the clouds and the late night rain had eased the misery of the summer time heat.

The old man was determined to take advantage of the unseasonably cool weather. He knew he might not have many more chances to look over the town. He adjusted his old-fashioned three-cornered hat and equally archaic breech coat just inside the doorway. Leaning heavily on his sturdy wooden cane, he shuffled out the door and reached for the wooden railing with his gnarled left hand. Leandre, his young African-American domestic slave, reached out and steadied him as he leaned against the rail.

"You sure you're ready for this, Commandant?" he asked.

"Oh, I'm ready," eighty-nine-year-old Jean Baptiste Vallé answered with a wry chuckle, followed by a bronchial cough.

He looked to the South, down what was once *Grande Rue,* where Main Street – as they called it now – disappeared off a steep hill. From below the precipice he could hear the South Gabouri Creek roaring with unusual summer vigor. Although he couldn't see the surging water, he didn't need to. He knew all about rushing waters.

Getting his bearings, the old man stared to the East. He knew what was out *there*. He smiled at the thought of the great river. Few men living knew it better than he. Turning north, he followed the path of *Grande Rue* as far as his fading eyes could focus. He knew that some two miles beyond was the fine stone home of his son, François Baptiste.

Turning on the narrow step and gazing through his own expansive yard and garden, he finally faced west. Toward *her*. Toward his past and his future. *Jeanne.* He stared fondly at the large oak tree in the yard, but instead saw his wife's tombstone on the other side of town in his mind. *Seven years. Seven long years.*

Suddenly remembering the presence of his male servant, the old gentleman tensed himself just as he felt his eyes getting watery. He cleared his throat, turned, and began the arduous task of getting his arthritic knees to take him down the steps. At the bottom of the steps, he stopped and looked back at the faithful companion.

"Yes, Leandre," he said softly, but with certainly. "I *am* ready."

"Sampson's bringing the carriage," Leandre said a minute later, as the old man caught his breath in front of his French Creole home.

"This house has stood for more than fifty years," the commandant said appraisingly, reaching out and feeling one of the palisaded fence posts in front of it. He grinned. "Maybe it will stand fifty more."

"My father helped build that house, Commandant," the black man replied, also taking a hard look at the structure. "I'm sure it will."

Commandant. It's been more than forty years and they still call me commandant. Jean Baptiste Vallé's mind went back to distant times as he shuffled across Main Street – it would always be *Grande Rue* to him— and glanced around the old neighborhood. One of Francis Cromer' s workers was loading a wagon in front of the small brick building at the corner. He could remember Renee LeMeilleur building it and the frame house next to it some thirty years earlier. The LeMeilleurs were long gone. Vallé had bought the two buildings himself in the 1830s and had given them to the Sisters of Loretto in 1837. They had stayed in the two buildings until the previous fall, selling to Cromer and moving across town.

The Bolduc family was still in the big house next to the former convent, though. Old Louis Bolduc had been the wealthiest man in town when he died in 1815. The commandant knew that honor was now his own, but rarely thought along those lines. They had done all right in Ste. Genevieve – the Vallés and the Bolducs and the Beauvais and the Prattes. They had prospered in the original village on the river bank and had been among the last to move up to the new village in the 1790s. They had done well here, too.

Vallé could sense Leandre beside him without turning around.

"You should have been here in the nineties, Leandre," he said, looking around the neighborhood. "It was quite a busy time. We didn't want to leave the old town, you know, despite all the flooding and erosion. It was easy for the young couples who had nothing to pack up and leave. But we had a lot of time and money invested down there."

He pointed in the direction of the river, *le Grand Champ*, where Vallé still owned a sizeable stretch of farm land, and the old village site, now nearly washed away by the river. Leandre stood silently, knowing his master would be discoursing for a spell. The commandant, he noted, had become rather long-winded in his old age.

"My brother François moved up from the old town in 1792 – without Commandant Peyroux's permission," he continued, chuckling. "Oh *my* Peyroux was he hot when he found out! The Bolducs moved the next year and Jeanne and I finally moved up here in ninety-four. The Prattes moved about that time, too, and the Beauvais. Of course the Spanish fort and the church were built then, too ..."

"The carriage has been waiting for some time, Commandant," Leandre interrupted after the commandant had continued for some time.

"You should have stopped me sooner, Leandre," the old man said with a phlegmy laugh. "I could go on for hours!"

The carriage had barely started to wobble down muddy Main Street when the old man signaled for Sampson, a much older African-American slave, to pull over in front of the former Vital St. Gemme Beauvais house. Augustine Menard was coming out the gate.

"Good morning, my dear!" he greeted her.

"Monsieur Vallé!" she exclaimed with delight. "It's so good to see you out and about! You look well."

"Now now, I'll have you know I *do* still have mirrors in my house, madam," he replied with feigned severity. "So I know perfectly well what *I* look like!"

He chuckled and his rheumy eyes gleamed for a moment.

"You, on the other hand, are truly a vision to behold," he added suavely.

"Monsieur Vallé," she said with a giggle, "you seem to become more charming as you grow older. And I have mirrors in my house, too – although I may start draping something over them!"

She looked down appraisingly as her rotund stomach.

"When is it due?" the commandant asked with a chuckle.

"October," she answered. "Then I'll have twice as much work to keep me busy."

Both shared a chuckle and the young woman leaned against the picket fence, enjoying the chance to see the old gentleman alert and chipper again.

"I cannot go past this house without thinking of your dear great grandparents," he said in a moment. "They were fine people. Vital and Felicité. And, of course, I always think of the little English boy."

The attractive young woman chuckled at the mere mention of the English boy. She had grown up hearing stories from her own grandparents, as well as the Vallés.

"Henry Marie Brackenridge," the commandant said, smiling fondly. "His father sent him here from Pittsburgh to learn French. It was not long after the Beauvais had moved up here – before Jeanne and I moved."

He stopped.

"Listen to me, I'm babbling again," he said, chuckling.

"No, no!" she insisted, jumping to her feet and stepping toward the carriage. "I love hearing these stories. I wish I could go back and visit old Ste. Genevieve."

"Child, not many young people are interested in the past," he said with a smile. "It's usually just old men like me who live in the past."

"I believe you taught him how to swim?" she asked, noticing Sampson roll his eyes in exasperation to see her urging him on.

"Oh yes!" he replied happily. "Up in the North Gabouri. I was still a young man then and often took the neighborhood children swimming. I'll tell you, as hot as it's been this summer, if I were about ten years younger, I'd have been swimming in the creek, myself!"

Leaning against the carriage, the six-months pregnant Augustine Menard carefully listened to the old tales she had heard many times before.

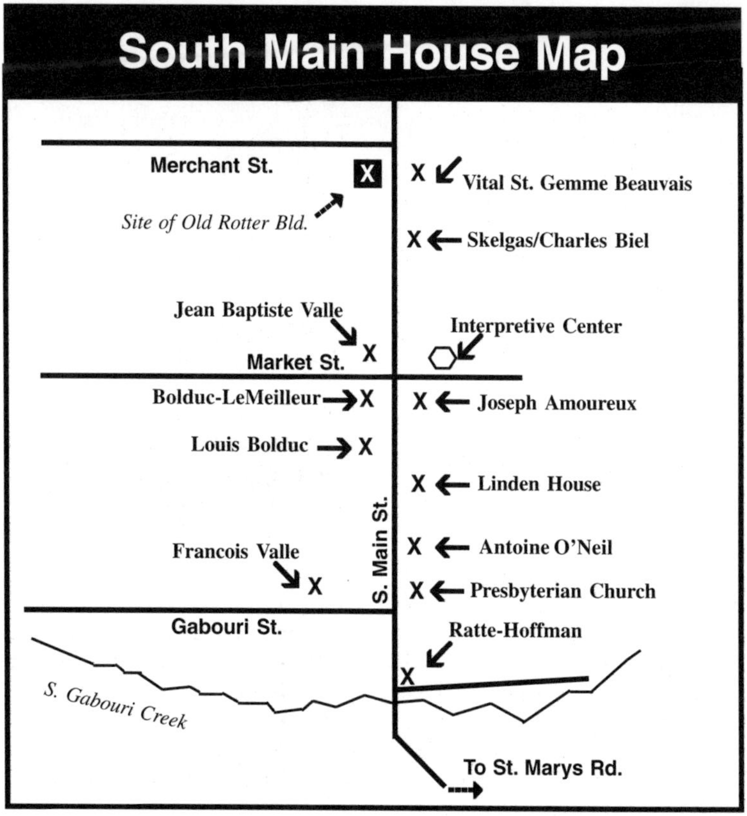

South Main House Map

Merchant St.
X
Site of Old Rotter Bld.
X Vital St. Gemme Beauvais
X Skelgas/Charles Biel
Jean Baptiste Valle X
Market St.
Interpretive Center
Bolduc-LeMeilleur X
X Joseph Amoureux
Louis Bolduc X
X Linden House
S. Main St.
Francois Valle X
X Antoine O'Neil
X Presbyterian Church
Gabouri St.
Ratte-Hoffman X
S. Gabouri Creek
To St. Marys Rd.

Louis Bolduc House Museum

125 S. Main

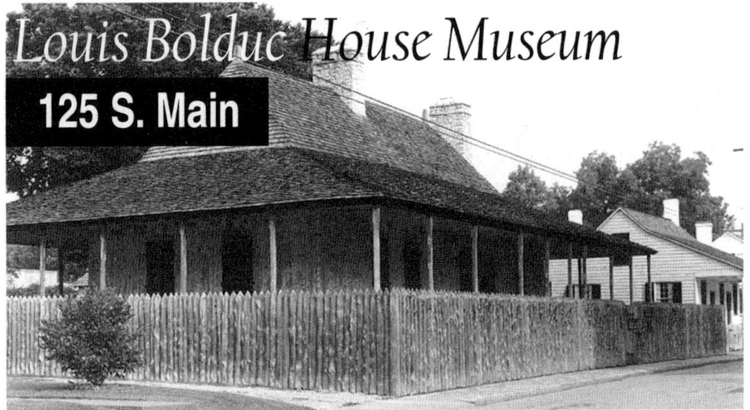

Ste. Genevieve's pride and joy, the 1793 Louis Bolduc House Museum, owned and operated by The National Society of Colonial Dames of America in The State of Missouri, is considered by many to be the finest French Creole restoration in the Mississippi Valley. A painstaking restoration in the 1950s made it the city's first museum house and an inspiration for later restorations.

Louis Bolduc was the wealthiest resident of Ste. Genevieve when the gradual move from the old town to the new began. A contract survives for the 1770 vertical log home he had constructed in the old town. Experts now agree that the current-day Bolduc House was built on the spot about 1793 – not disassembled and moved from the old town, as legend had it.

Some components, though, have been tree ring dated earlier than the rest of the timber. It appears likely, therefore, that Bolduc did salvage some wood from his flood-damaged 1770 home in the old town. The white oak ceiling timbers of the south half of the house certainly appear to have been salvaged from that 1770 home.

Dr. Richard Guyette, the University of Missouri expert who did dendrochronology (tree ring studies) tests of the Bolduc and other homes in Ste. Genevieve during the

Marguerite Appleton, national president of the National Society of Colonial Dames of America (left), the Rt. Rev. Edmund J. Venverloh, and Mrs. Harry B. Mathews, Jr., cut the ribbon to open the Bolduc House Museum in May 1958.

"squared timbers with all the sapwood removed...Ax marks and exposed termite tunnels indicate the sapwood was removed after the termite damage was done." One white oak wall log, meanwhile, dates to 1788 – a likely replacement for a flood-damaged log on Bolduc's old house which was still worth salvaging in 1792.

Bolduc died in 1815, but the house remained in his family until 1949, when Mary C. Reber purchased the sagging old home and gave it to the Colonial Dames. With the backing of Mrs. & Mrs. Harry Mathews, the Dames began a painstaking restoration process. In 1956 Dr. Ernest Allen Connally, a Rice and Harvard graduate, HABS veteran and future associate director of the National Park Service, was brought in to oversee the project.

"He had a truly distinguished career," Dr. Osmund Overby, another nationally-respected architectural historian, speaking of Connally. "It was really the Bolduc House that began drawing national attention to him. It was an extremely well-informed and competent restoration."

"In the Bolduc, I simply had to let the building itself tell me what it was," Connally said in a telephone interview with the author, two years before his death in 1999. "There were very few documentary records of any kind about the house. We had to depend on the building itself. It provided all the evidence we needed, for the correct slope of the building was in the building.

"The building itself told us the position of doors, the correct dimensions of widows and told us it [the *galerie*] was open."

While the *galerie* apparently had no roof, the attic was used for storing grain. Some dried, shriveled

The Bolduc brings out the eighteenth century in many people.

OVERLEAF: The Louis Bolduc House prior to restoration

The Bolduc's Norman truss is one of several spectacular trusses in town.

kernels of corn were found there during the restoration.

A grand opening was held in October 1957 and the Bolduc House was officially opened to the public in the spring of 1958.

Connally honored

Dr. Ernest Allen Connally, seen here making an address at the dedication of the Bolduc House Museum in 1958, was honored in 2001 by the National Society of Colonial Dames in the State of Missouri. Connally, who died in 1999, posthumously received the organization's second historic preservation award.

Bolduc-LeMeilleur House

101 S. Main

Built in 1820 by Rene LeMeilleur, son-in-law of Louis Bolduc, this house was restored in the 1960s in a project led by the renowned Ernest Allen Connally. Prior to its restoration, the building was a two-story frame I-house with a huge two-story porch – sagging near the end of its life. Next to it was a two-story brick building.

The original brick structure was apparently one story and may have been built at the same time as the frame house, ten feet from it. It was definitely there by 1825, when the lot was divided, with Jean Baptiste Valle buying the portion with the brick building. He is believed to have rented it to Matthew Ziegler, owner of the Green Tree Inn, for

The Bolduc-LaMeilleur when it served as a hotel.

tobacco manufacturing. Valle later acquired the frame building, too, and deeded both to the Sisters of Loretto in 1837. They served as a Lorettine school, named Our Lady of Mount Carmel. The Lorettines sold the lot to Francis I. Cromer in October, 1848 and moved across town. After bouncing between several owners, the structures became the Detchmendy House Hotel.

Connally concluded that the second story was added to the brick store building at that time. The frame structure, he suggested, did not pick up its two-story appearance until about 1870. "Structural evidence for all this is quite clear," Connally reported at the time. "We can be sure it (the brick building) was not enlarged before 1850." He was similarly convinced about the frame structure.

During the restoration of 1966-67, it was stripped to its barest components and restored in what some would call "creeping reconstruction." The old brick structure was razed to make the north side of the house visible. Connally noted that so little could be uncovered of the original circa 1820 brick building that saving it and taking it back to its original appearance would have been "wholly impractical." Connally also felt the frame structure was the more important for interpreting the town's architectural progress.

"It illustrates residential evolution as the settlers absorbed the influences of the United States," he said at the time. "This may be regarded as a typical family home of the period."

The walls are built according to American practices, with widely-spaced hand-hewn posts rather than the vertical logs used in the Creole style. It is now owned by The National Society of Colonial Dames of America in the State of Missouri.

Not enough original fabric of the brick building could be saved to make restoration feasible. It served as a garage during its final years. This was one of the last photos of it before its demolition.

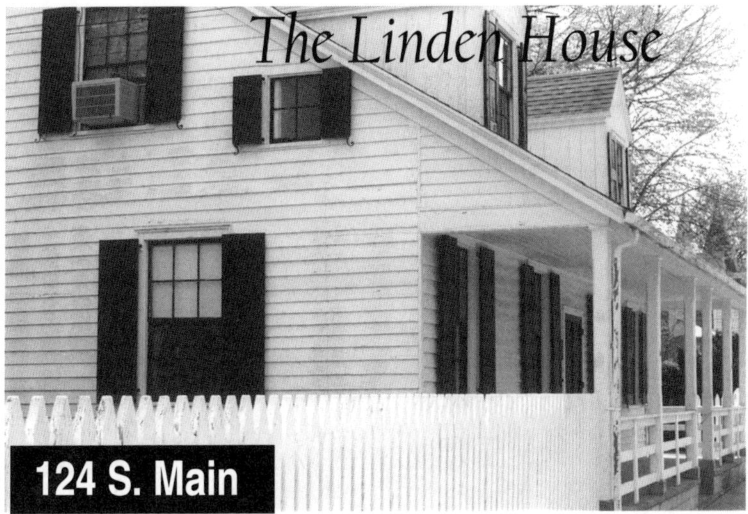

Restored by The National Society of Colonial Dames of America in the State of Missouri, the Linden House dates to the 1810s. The brick-nogged, heavy-timber frame house originally consisted of a single story hall-and-parlor unit with a central chimney. The northern side of the present house dates to about 1813, with a first addition believed to have been constructed in the mid nineteenth century.

The current roof system and western façade came into being at that time. A central hall was also added, along with the southern half of the house. Evidence of Greek Revival influence may be seen in doors in the central hallway. Material still seems to exist from the original structure, though. A handmade six-panel door, thought to be the original entrance to the home, is still in the cellar. Cellar joists under the northern side of the house, meanwhile, are hand-hewn and appear to date from that period, as well. The house was later expanded to include two frame enlargements and a brick wing.

Known historically as the Gemien Beauvais House, it is used extensively by the Colonial Dames as a meeting and entertaining site and is occasionally open to the public.

TheLinden House is decorated with Christmas finery each year, such as this goosefeather tree.

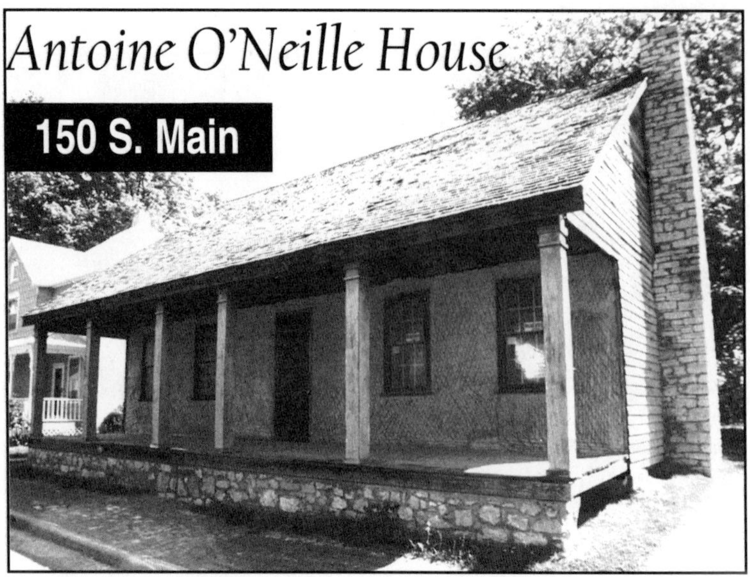

Damaged in a fire in 1982, this Anglo-American vernacular I-house goes back to the 1810s.

Built of heavy timber frame construction, it sits on a lot purchased by Antoine O'Neille in 1810. The house is first mentioned in a deed from 1820.

The 1982 fire allowed the HABS team to get a good look at the house's structure. It appeared that the building was originally a single-story, five-bay structure, with the upper half-story added at a later date.

The house was restored in the 1980s, following the fire, and is awaiting a use. Although it is not one of the city's French Creole structures, it definitely contributes to the historic character and charm of South Main.

South Main, circa 1832, as seen in the Lewis Pruneau diorama.

Joseph Amoureux House

102 S. Main

Also known as the Etienne Parent House, this attractive structure was built about 1844 in a Greek Revival side-passage style similar to the Gregoire House at 51 South Fourth Street. Common in St. Louis, the side-passage town houses were rare in Ste. Genevieve. The brick structure – stripped of aluminum awnings and sidings during a restoration by current owners Bob and Odile Mecker – has been both a residence and a business structure.

It includes flat limestone door and window lintels, with a recessed side passage entry way and the entrance door surrounded by a transom and sidelights. Much of the interior glass and floor plan have survived and a few pedimented, Greek Revival door heads still exist. The joists are vertical sawn. Reports that the roof is copper, turned green with age, however, have been disproved. The roof is merely painted green.

First Presbyterian Church

160 S. Main

Built in a Gothic Revival style in 1904, this church received an added annex in 1954. The brick structure is one of the older Protestant churches in Ste. Genevieve and offers such Gothic stylistic elements as a corner tower and traceried stained glass windows. Wedged into the corner of this historic South Main block, it adds to the overall historic and aesthetic aura of the neighborhood.

The Jean Baptiste Valle House is an eye-catching relic, so synonymous with Ste. Genevieve. The *poteaux sur solle,* or "posts on a sill" home is graced by a colonial-style garden and wooden fence, keeping largely intact the colonial flavor of the historic district.

Constructed in 1794, the house was the home of Ste. Genevieve's final colonial commandant, Jean Baptiste Valle (1760-1849). The host of this book, he succeeded his brother, Francois Valle II, as commandant just days before France turned the territory over to the United States in 1804. He was then appointed to continue in his duties by the new American government for several months and lived until 1849.

A giant oak, called the "Council Tree," was supposedly where the Valle boys used their legendary diplomatic skills making deals with area Indians. It graced the yard until just a few years ago. A circa-1812 barn on the lot was destroyed by a storm in the 1970s and was replaced by a combination shed and garage, which strongly resembles the original structure.

The basement is made of four-feet thick rubblestone, with three-quarter-round masonry buttresses. The design of basement led to persistent rumors that it had been used as a fort prior to the house itself standing on the spot. Historians today give this tale no credence. The basement shows evidence that the grand old house was constructed in three different stages.

The important J.B. Valle House has been owned by only three families. The great house was modified extensively by Leon Vion in the late 1800s. His granddaughter Vion Papin Schramm and her husband Bernard have lived there more than thirty years. Mrs. Schramm has cultivated one of the town's most outstanding gardens, in keeping with Ste. Genevieve colonial traditions.

Jean Baptiste Valle almost assuredly had the honor of being the first Ste. Genevieve resident to pose for a photograph. This daguerreotype was taken in the mid or late 1840s -- probably in St. Louis. It was the basis for Bernard Peters' 1938 painting of Valle that hangs in the Guibourd-Valle House. That painting, in turn, inspired this book's cover art work by Janet Kraus. This photograph of the original daguerreotype is owned by the Missouri Historical Society.

The 200-year-old structure stands in the heart of Ste. Genevieve's historic district, which began to take shape in the early 1790s. Stories that the original town site was abandoned virtually overnight after the disastrous 1785 flood are ludicrous. Plenty of evidence has been gleaned in recent decades, proving that the move had already begun in modest fashion before the great flood, and that it continued for a full decade.

The gradual exodus from the old town site to the new was begun by the less affluent residents. Presumably, they had shacks or small cabins, if not mean lean-tos in the old village and probably constructed the same type lodging in the new. It was when the wealthy merchants, planters and other local elite began to give up on their larger investments in the old town, that the face of the new town was permanently stamped. As men like Louis Bolduc, Nicolas and Francois Janis, Vital St. Gemme Beauvais and the Valle brothers used their wealth and their slave manpower to construct well-built homes in the early 1790s, an architectural legacy was left that would make tiny Ste. Genevieve unique in North America.

Thankfully, an upstairs fire in January, 1999 was unable to rob Ste. Genevieve and the world in general of one of those treasures. It did no structural damage and the Schramms escaped without injury. The grand old house continues to help anchor the heart of historic Ste. Genevieve.

The J.B. Valle House, as miniature artist Lewis Pruneau depicted it in his 1832 Ste. Genevieve diorama. The house had already been enlarged, but still had its French colonial appearance.

Did you know?

When the local bank was robbed in 1873 (supposedly by the James Gang), the loot was allegedly divided in the back yard of the J.B. Valle House.

Skelgas/Charles Biel Store

This tri-gable ell commercial structure, covered with deteriorating Depression era tar paper siding, once housed a thriving mercantile business owned by Charles H. Biel. Born in Germany in 1838, Biel came to America at age fifteen and settled in Ste. Genevieve in 1879. He held several positions, including county coroner and deputy sheriff and was a member of the local school board.

Old photos show the store as a booming place, with the Biel family apparently living upstairs. Built in the 1880s or early 1890s, the tri-gable building maintains its original shape behind the decrepit siding. It was later called The Ratchet Store

Vital St. Gemme Beauvais House

20 S. Main

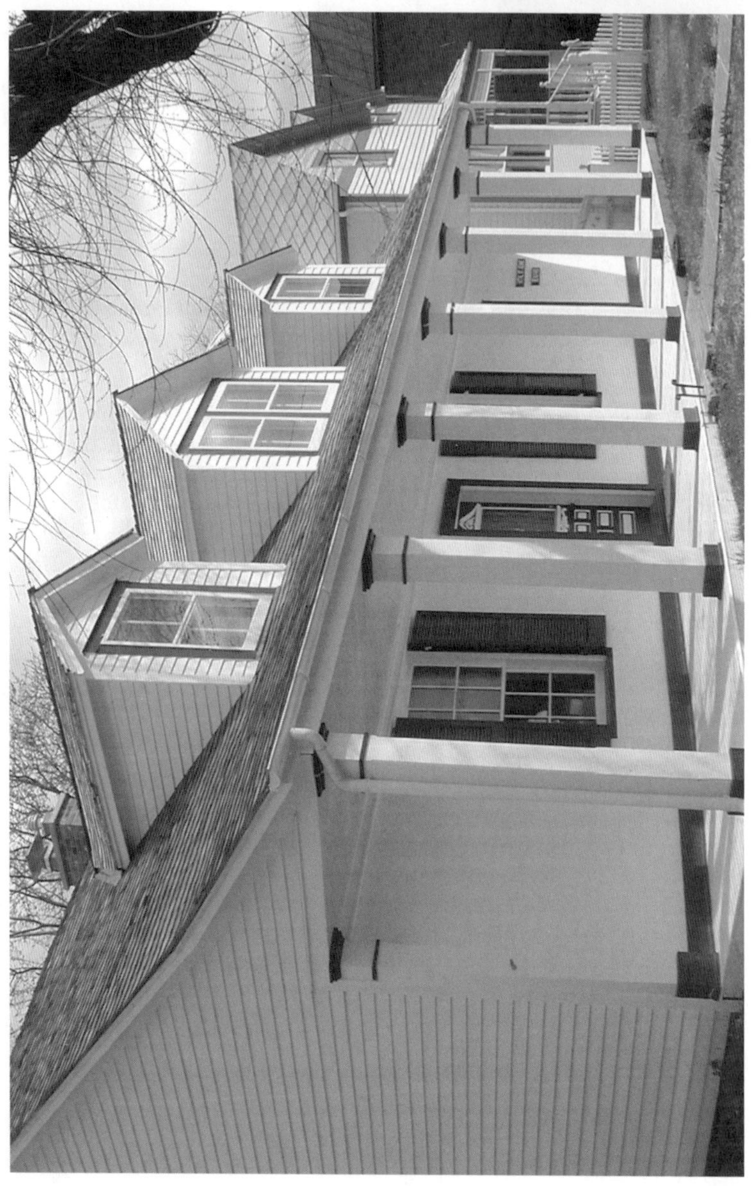

One of the most storied homes in Ste. Genevieve, the Beauvais House has gained and maintained significance in many ways over the years. As one of the three *poteaux en terre* (posts-in-the-ground) buildings in Ste. Genevieve and one of five surviving examples in the United States, it has tremendous architectural significance. This is despite major remodeling jobs done to the house in the late nineteenth and early twentieth century.

Dendrochronology during the 1980s dated the French Creole structure to 1792, with the northern half thought to be added about 1800. Like the other Ste. Genevieve *poteaux en terre* houses, the Beauvais is made of sturdy red cedar. The roof was remodeled in the late 1800s and the king-post trusses and wind braces cut. The remaining portion of the original roof system is still visible in the attic, though. A late nineteenth century photo clearly shows the old French roof line still visible after the alterations. Unlike many of the French Creole houses, the Beauvais' vertical logs are infilled not with *bouzillage,* but with *pierrotage,* a mixture of stone and lime mortar.

The house is also significant as being the home of Vital St. Gemme Beauvais, one of the leading citizens of colonial Ste. Genevieve, and the temporary home of Henry Marie Brackenridge. Brackenridge, who would go on to make a name for himself in business and in writing, was sent to Ste. Genevieve in 1792 by his father, a Pittsburgh judge. He wanted the boy to learn French. Henry did so, despite knowing only *oui* and *non* upon his arrive. However, yes and no were the only words of English he remembered two years later, when he returned to Pittsburgh.

Two hundred year old *poteaux en terre* logs still frame the Beauvais House.

Brackenridge grew up to write *Recollection of Persons and Places of the West*, in which he left a hugely important child's eye view of colonial Ste. Genevieve. He also paid a sentimental return visit as a young man in 1811.

The house continued to shelter important local citizens, even after Vital Beauvais' death in 1816. Among these were Louis C. and Augustine Menard. Louis Menard (1819-1870) was a son of legendary Kaskaskia leader Pierre Menard and was briefly mayor of Ste. Genevieve. He was a leading local businessman, "universally esteemed and highly respected," according to *Goodspeed's History of Southeast Missouri*. His widow, Augustine, was the great granddaughter of Vital St. Gemme Beauvais and was considered the town's leading historian in her old age – along with her brother, Captain Augustus St. Gemme. During the 1880s, several mentions were made in local newspapers of her pear tree, said to be over 100 years old at the time.

This huge beam still runs the entire length of the Beauvais basement. Hollowed by termites it is no longer load-bearing.

"Mrs. Menard is a woman of wonderful memory, and is perhaps, the best posted person, regarding the history of this country of anyone now living. She is pleasing in her conversation and can relate many valuable and interesting anecdotes of the early history of Ste. Genevieve. She is well known to the historical societies of Chicago, Wisconsin and St. Louis, having furnished them much valuable information."

The house was later owned by William and Sophia Wilder, who lobbed fourteen feet off of the north side of the house in 1900. A rotting kingpost was the culpret, making the change necessarily, according to newspaper accounts. At the same time, thc Wilders added the current kitchen – which the current owners are restoring to the 1900 time period.

F. Anton Weiler, a local banker and longtime county commissioner, bought the home in 1917 and lived there until his death in 1964.

Since then it has undergone restorations by Frankye and Norbert Donze, Al Keiser, Jerry and Jackie Grindstaff and – most recently – William Lemire and Yvonne Tomich. In fact, Lemire and Tomich, the current owners, received the 2001 Preserve Missouri Award for their restoration. They plan to reside in the historic home. It is occasionally open for tours.

Augustine Menard Bldg. 2 S. Main

Although this attractive Italianate commercial building on the corner of Main and Merchant bears the name of Mrs. Augustine Menard, it is not certain what, if any, contact she had with it. The wife of Louis C. Menard, she was considered one to the town's leading historians in her old age (See page 20), living in the Vital St. Gemme Beauvais House. Late nineteenth century biographical sketches of her mention nothing of her running a business of her own.

The brick building, though, is an excellent example of the ornate Victorian era commercial buildings that anchored most communities' downtown business districts. Ste. Genevieve is fortunate enough to have several downtown corners distinguished by attractive turn of the century store fronts.

The Italianate influence of this building can be seen in the wide, bracketed cornice on the facade. Probably built about 1875, its two-light windows on the upper floors seem to be original. The shop windows on the first floor were apparently added later.

Hotel Ste. Genevieve 1 N. Main

Built in 1901, the former Audubon Hotel was gutted by a disastrous fire in January 1956 and was completely redone inside.

The commercial vernacular structure is Ste. Genevieve's largest historic hotel building and anchors the confluence of three important neighborhoods – the French Creole survivors of South Main, the German, Anglo and Commercial vernacular brick section of North Main, and the mixed residential and commercial district along Merchant Street.

Some of the brick work detail is still visible in the facade, such as the string course between floors and the quoins.

Sampson turned onto Merchant Street and gestured toward the attractive ashlar stone home of the commandant's fourth son, Felix Vallé. The old man nodded his head and climbed out of the carriage as soon as it had stopped. Yes, the Vallé family had done well. Felix, even more than his other sons, had shown the commandant's knack for turning a profit. The family legacy begun by his father, François Vallé I, *lieutenant particulier* of the old village, seemed to be alive and well.

"Papa!" Odile Pratte Vallé cried a moment later, after the old man had entered the building. She hurried over and embraced him. "You are looking well!"

"It is much cooler," he replied with a smile. "Even an old man may be rejuvenated in such weather."

"Well it's wonderful to see you out and about. We've been saying prayers for you, and … We've been saying prayers for you."

She added the repeated sentence quickly, but the old man wasn't fooled.

"What else have you been praying for, dear?" he asked, having a good idea of what it was.

"The town itself," she said reluctantly, looking at her shoes.

"I see," he said. "Did my newspapers arrive?"

Her grim expression told him what he needed to know.

He followed her into the residential side of the stone building and sat down in a wing backed chair. She silently handed him the St. Louis newspapers. Putting his glasses on, he scanned them quickly.

"Twenty-two cholera deaths," he read aloud, shaking his head. He had heard such rumors. Despite what many seemed to think, he was still quite alert, even when confined to bed. He skimmed through other issues. "It seems to be waning."

"Or migrating," his daughter-in-law replied.

"Well, praying is about all we can do unless it does hit," he said, hoisting himself out of the chair. "Felix is still in St. Louis?"

Nodding her head, she quickly turned away and faced the wall.

"My child, take heart," he said, laying a bony hand on her quivering shoulders. "Our Felix is a healthy and smart young man. He will return safely. And the Chouteaus, no doubt, will look after him while he is there. Plus, as we said, it seems to have run its course up there."

Odile turned around and embraced him. "Thank you," she said, dabbing her eye. "I know God will protect him. And us."

In a few moments the commandant excused himself and stepped back into the breezy coolness of the morning. The first building he saw was the former home of Lewis Linn. He involuntarily shuddered. *The cholera.*

Lord, let it not come back. It had been horrendous in 1843. The good Dr. Linn, a United States Senator, had left his Washington duties to come home and help fight the epidemic, only to die under the strain, himself.

Pushing such morose thoughts out of his mind, he crossed Merchant Street to the impressive two and half-story stone building caddycorner across the street. Dr. Linn at one time had owned it, as well. After greeting friends there, he stepped back outside and saw the widow Shaw hanging out wash behind her white frame house on the opposite corner.

"Your wash may get wet, madam," he said, hobbling through her yard. His heart went out to Emilie Shaw. A daughter of the old innkeeper Francois Janis, she had already been widowed once when she married Dr. Benjamin Shaw several years ago. Now she was a widow again. Dr. Shaw had died in March, leaving her and their young son to fend for themselves.

"They're already wet, Colonel Vallé," she replied, using the commandant's other familiar title. "And they're not likely to dry indoors."

"No, I would think not," he replied. He missed the quick wit and sharp humor that had characterized her before the doctor' s death. He hoped she would eventually regain her good spirits. "I hope you are well today."

"I'm well," she said, taking a moment to catch her breath. "Just tired. And you? I had heard you were ill."

"Just old," he replied. "I suppose I'm doing as well as can be expected for someone nearly ninety."

The widow Shaw gave him an apprising look, as if trying to picture what it would feel like to be ninety. "I'm glad you are out and about," she said.

Taking his leave, Vallé moved back toward the street, where he heard a familiar voice call his name. He turned and cackled with glee to see his old friend Jean Ferdinand Rozier standing in front of his house.

The two elderly men met in front of the old Parfait Dufour house, next door to the white frame Rozier home.

"We get cool weather and look what we find out prowling the streets!" Rozier snapped, laughing and patting the commandant on the back.

"The sheriff had better be on alert with the likes of us on the street!" Vallé replied with glee.

"The cool weather is much easier on old bones, no?" Rozier asked, gesturing toward himself.

"Old?" the commandant snapped. "My dear Rozier, you are nearly twenty years my junior! Unlike you, *I* was still putting in an honest day's work when I was your age!"

The two men — definitely the two wealthiest in town —shared a laugh and Rozier offered the commandant a pinch of snuff.

"Have you heard from Jules recently?" he asked. One of Rozier' s sons, Jules, was in California, trying to cash in on the gold rush. Letters so far had not been encouraging.

"He sounds discouraged," Rozier said with a shrug. "Yet he still

The two elderly men met in front of the old Parfait Dufour house, next door to the white frame Rozier home.

digs. I suspect he will come home when he gets his fill. I don't understand him sometimes."

"Now I recall a young French navy man who was never adverse to adventure or the lure of far-off profit," Vallé reminded him. "I'll wager *he* would be in California at this very minute."

Rozier had to chuckle. The commandant was making an obvious reference to Rozier's early days when he and fellow Napoleonic navy veteran John James Audubon had come to America to forge their way as traders and businessmen.

"Perhaps you are right, old friend," Rozier replied with a smile. "Actually I think we *both* would be there, panning for gold, were we each twenty-two again!"

The two old friends quietly enjoyed their snuff and the cool breeze for a moment, waving at passersby.

"Have you heard from Audubon?" Vallé finally asked.

"Back in the spring," Rozier answered. "He is doing well. He said he will send another bird this summer."

Vallé leaned against the fence and cackled with glee.

"I was telling young Leandre about Audubon just the other day," he said, "about how you would go off on a business trip and return to find the store closed up and him off in the woods, painting birds and trees."

"I've heard you tell that tale before and you exaggerate a bit," Rozier said with a chuckle. "He was a good partner, despite his other interests. But I know he's been much happier since he gave up on merchandizing."

"A man must enjoy what he does, if he is to succeed at it," Vallé said with a nod. "Your Firmin seems to enjoy his new ventures."

"You would think a law office would be enough to occupy one," Rozier said, shaking his head, "especially after devoting so much energy toward building the plank road to Farmington. Yet he insists on restoring that school. And now he's talking about running for the state assembly next year."

"Really?" the commandant gasped. "Well he certainly has the potential to serve well – like dear Dr. Linn and John Scott and the others."

Their conversation was interrupted several times as those walking or driving by would stop to greet the two patriarchs. The sun made a brief appearance and the commandant began to perspire. Shortly Sampson appeared and suggested that it might be time for a nip of claret and a nap.

Merchant Street Map

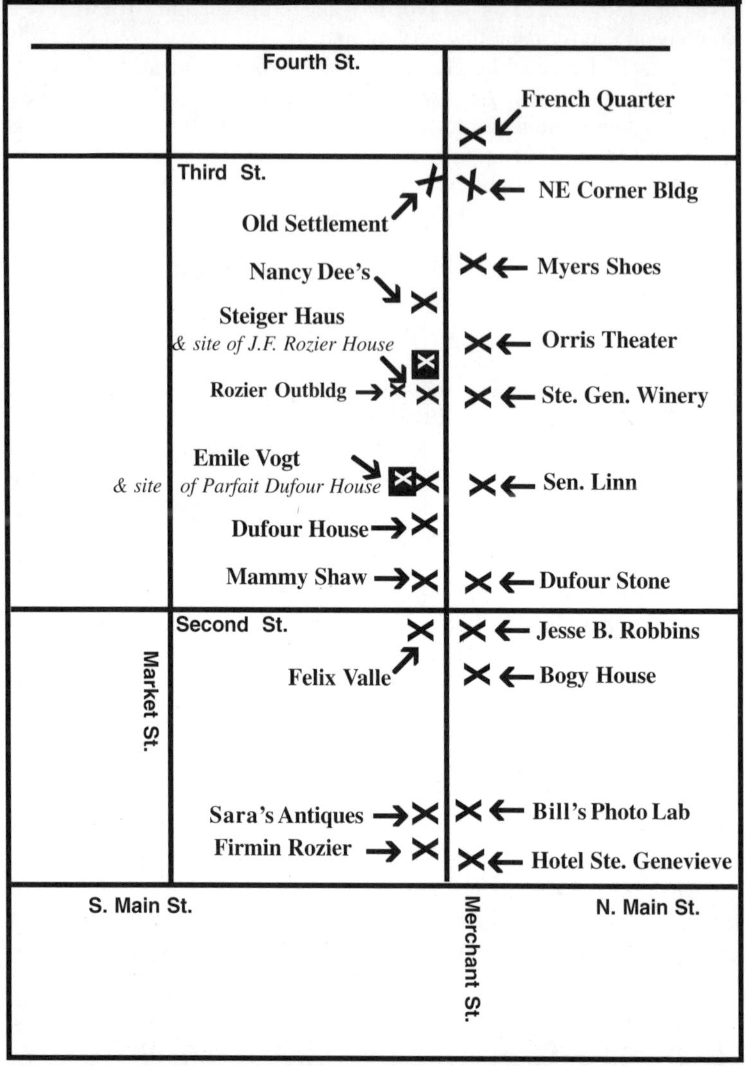

Fourth St.

French Quarter

Third St.

Old Settlement

NE Corner Bldg

Nancy Dee's

Myers Shoes

Steiger Haus
& site of J.F. Rozier House

Orris Theater

Rozier Outbldg

Ste. Gen. Winery

Emile Vogt
& site of Parfait Dufour House

Sen. Linn

Dufour House

Mammy Shaw

Dufour Stone

Second St.

Jesse B. Robbins

Felix Valle

Bogy House

Market St.

Sara's Antiques

Bill's Photo Lab

Firmin Rozier

Hotel Ste. Genevieve

S. Main St.

Merchant St.

N. Main St.

NOTE: Market and Merchant are both one-way streets. Market goes West to East; Merchant goes East to West.

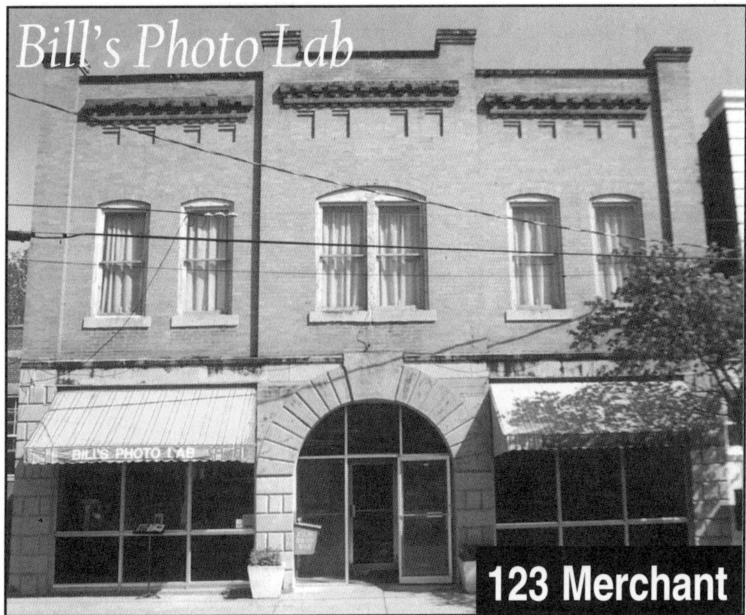

Said to have originally been built as the Post Office, this commercial vernacular building was built during the first decade of the twentieth century.

It has "a rather showy commercial façade," in the words of the HABS report. Some of the original grandeur was lost with the addition of modern windows and doors on the first floor and is somewhat dwarfed by the Hotel Ste. Genevieve, which connects with it.

Still, the brick building lends elegance and strength to the street with its lightly projecting entrance bay, broken façade roof lie and arched entrance.

Historic and picturesque Merchant Street is often photographed by visitors and locals alike.

Firmin Rozier Building

124 Merchant

Now hosting Sara's Ice Cream Shop, this sturdy brick building was built about 1850, after General Firmin A. Rozier had launched a local law practice. (He was joined by his younger brother Charles in 1850, which might have led to the new building being constructed.)

The HABS report notes that while Rozier was French, he apparently hired German bricklayers to construct the brick building. It is similar to the Pierre Schumert and John Hael Houses on North Main.

The window openings may be original, although the plate glass windows are not. Orginal exposed, beaded ceiling joists are visible inside.

Sara's Antiques

132 Merchant

The other half of Sara's Ice Cream/Antiques, this turn of the century building is less historic than its neighbor. Yet it well represents the ornate Victorian era storefronts of that period.

The pressed metal commercial façade is largely intact and adds elegance to the historic mercantile street.

Now home of the Bogy House Restaurant, this circa 1870 Italianate I-house includes two rooms from Joseph Bogy's circa 1810 log home on this spot.

As it took shape about 1870, the frame wall home has bracketed eaves, a central hall plan, two-light window sash and cast iron fence. This appearance probably dates to shortly after Jesse B. Robbins bought the lot from the Bogy family in 1869. The fine old home has its original clapboards.

Jesse Robbins House **199 Merchant**

This 1867 brick beauty is one of the few Italianate homes in Ste. Genevieve. As the HABS report notes, several Ste. Genevieve homes have Italianate ornament tacked on to vernacular house plans. The Robbins House, though, seems to have been built as a thoroughly Italianate house.

It retains its original bracket eaves, two-light window sash and porch with its fancy jigsaw cut-outs and bracketed eaves.

The Vallé and Menard families were two of the most important clans in Upper Louisiana and this attractive ashlar stone structure survives as a key testimony to the business dynasty the two families shared.

Built in 1818 by Jacob Phillipson, another early business leader in Ste. Genevieve, it was bought by Jean Baptiste Vallé in 1824 for the B.L. Vallé & Company firm. The three original partners in the firm, incorporated in 1817, were Pierre Menard, Jean Baptiste Valle, and his son, West Pointer Louis Vallé. The name changed sometime around 1820 to Menard & Valle. After Louis Vallé's untimely death in 1833 – supposedly after being bitten by a mad dog, the firm took on two new partners and operated as Menard, Vallé & Company. After his brother's death, Felix Vallé took over his position of running his father's interests in the firm.

After the firm dissolved, Felix and Odile Pratte Vallé continued living there. Eventually they modernized it with later nineteenth century stylistic elements. Felix died in1877, leaving Odile the wealthiest person in Ste. Genevieve. One local legend said she would stand on her front porch (since removed) and toss dimes to children headed to school. Whether she threw money or not, she certainly had it and certainly spent it. She paid for about three-quarters of the current Catholic church when it was built, 1876-1880, and traded land for the current Vallé Springs Cemetery to the city. This was to allow her to be buried beside Felix in the old memorial cemetery – closed to new burials since 1882. She died in 1894 and the home moved into the Rozier family. It was later purchased by the state and restored to its original Federal double pile appearance in 1973.

Now owned and run as a state historic site by the Missouri Department of Natural Resources (DNR),

Colonial era entertainment and costumes are frequently beheld at the Felix Valle.

the family and the right a mercantile shop. Upstairs, the Vallé's bedroom has been restored, including a huge period *armoire.*

Site Director Jim Baker's office has been moved from the Felix Vallé, across the street, to the Mammy Shaw House, allowing the entire building to be returned to period style.

Behind the building is a rare early nineteenth century outbuilding – quite an important historical survivor in itself. Archaeological work by Southeast Missouri State University students in 1998 and 1999 located the foundations of what appear to have been the stone kitchen and privy which formerly occupied parts of the lot.

the building is site of many special events, such as *Le Reveillon*, the traditional "wake up" breakfast in the French Catholic community, which followed Midnight Mass in colonial days. Period snacks are prepared for guests at the modern *Reveillon*, usually held in conjunction with Felix Vallé's birthday in February.

The downstairs has been restored as it might have been around 1830, with the east half a parlor for

A Southeast Missouri State University student sifts dirt in the Felix Valle yard during the 1998 archaeology field school.

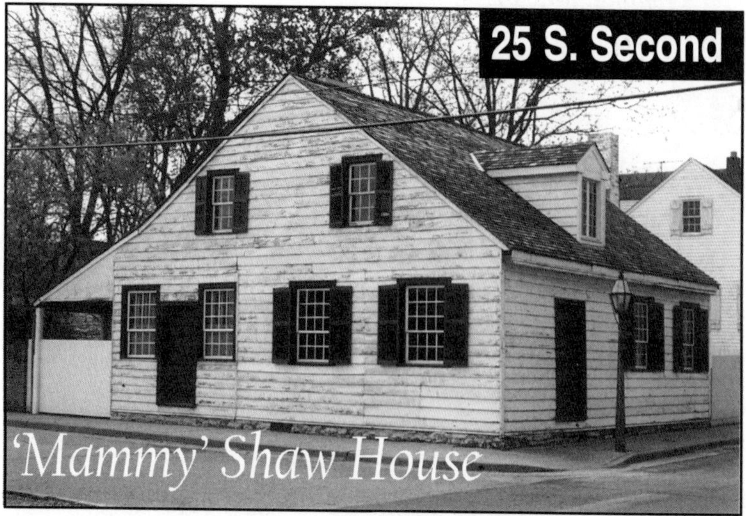

This small white house has gone through many periods and many uses over the years. The original section was built by Jean Baptiste Bossier in 1818 as a storehouse. After the DNR obtained the building in the late 1990s, the ghosts of Bossier's original shelves were discovered on the walls. A decrepit later addition on the rear was replaced with modern office space.

The enlargement was made after Bossier sold the lot to Dr. Benjamin Shaw in 1837. Shaw married the widow Emilie Janis LeCompte, daughter of former Green Tree Inn owner François Janis, in 1843, which may have been when they addition was built. Shaw died in 1849, leaving Emilie and one son on their own. She lived in the house another forty-eight years, until her death at age ninety in 1897. She was said to have been known as "Mammy" Shaw – although her obituary makes no mention of this.

Later the old home was owned by local artist Matt Ziegler. The renowned Ste. Genevieve Art Colony and art school was headquartered here during the 1930s and 1940s. Ziegler built a stone patio and corridor – supposedly of stones from the demolished Joseph Pratte Warehouse (See page 139) – connecting to an ornate stone kitchen. Formerly called the Indian Trading Post, the stone structure has been tree ring dated to 1841 – obviously the work of Dr. Shaw. Ziegler also added the Merchant Street dormer.

The original two-room section built by Bossier still has its original hand hewn sills and vertical sawn cellar joists, as well as vertical uprights on the heavy-timber frame. The original, random-width floor boarding also survives. A set of unusual etched glass doors supposedly came from the 1842 wreck of the steamboat Dr. Franklin II. The Shaw House boasts some of the most unusual – and certainly original – door hardware in Ste. Genevieve.

Dufour Stone Building

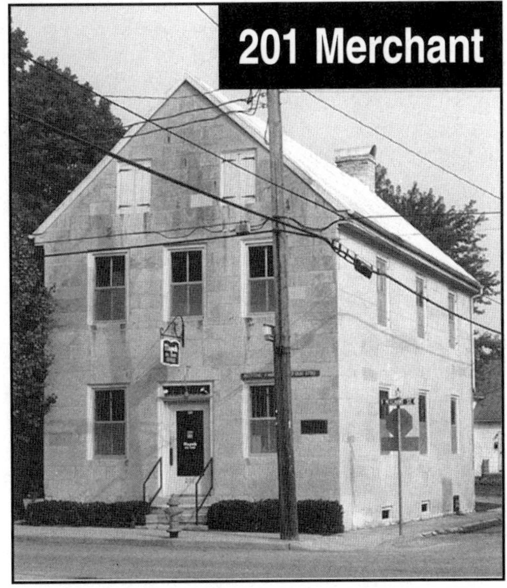

The intersection of Merchant and Second Streets signifies an important change in Ste. Genevieve life – and in life in all the Mississippi River towns. The ornate Dufour Stone Building, the equally attractive Felix Vallé House and the smaller Jean Baptiste Bossier (now Mammy Shaw) store were all built on this intersection in 1818. This was just two years after the Zebulon Pike became the first riverboat to make the New Orleans to St. Louis run. The arrival of riverboat travel and shipping signified a new era in commerce – and men like Jean Baptiste and Louis Vallé, Bossier and Henry Keil were ready to capitalize on it.

Like the Felix Vallé, this building, built by the firm of Keil, Bisch and Roberts, was a substantial investment and was intended to offer an imposing commercial presence. Both buildings have ashlar stone facades to the street. The Dufour building then has sharply contracting field sone on the other sides and rear. Like the Millard-Vallé House, this lends an eye-appealing contrast and makes this a most attractive building.

Colonial resident and former scout Parfait Dufour was long believed to have built this building – and he could have just before selling the lot to Keil, Bisch and Roberts in 1818. It seems more likely that the new firm built it shortly after that. Henry Keil went on to forge a tremendous career in St. Louis. The Keil Auditorium bears his name. In 1831 the last remaining partner, Edmund Roberts, sold it to Senator Lewis Linn. In 1891 it became Rozier Bank and was a bank for more than seventy-five years. It was not robbed by Jesse James in 1873; that robbery took place at the Old Rottler Building (See page __.) on Main and Merchant. It was robbed in 1939, though, with a bloody bullet-flying chase following. City Marshal Henry J. Drury was shot after catching up with the robbers six miles out of town. The marshal survived and the three men – who stole $2,200 – each got fifteen years in prison. The author has talked to old-timers who remember viewing the marshal's car afterward, saying it was shot full of holes like a piece of Swiss cheese. Today the building is home of Tlapek Real Estate.

The rough stone sides of the Dufour Stone Building are equally interesting.

Despite some interior and exterior changes, the HABS reports remarks that "it represents the remarkable survival of an important early nineteenth century commercial building with its original structural system almost completely intact." The building's original roof frame and vertical sawn cellar joists are still in use. The attic flooring is probably original, too. It may have been used for storage originally. The remains of a very old elevator pulley system in the attic may have been used in the mid or late nineteenth century to lift heavy objects to the attic.

Theophilus Dufour House

While definite proof has not yet been established, it appears likely that the home of noted eighteenth century scout Antoine "Parfait" Dufour was located where the Emile Vogt House now stands (next door), rather than on the site of his son Theophilus' house. That confusion has led this quaint frame house to be dated as early as the 1780s by some local researchers. Most scholars believe it was built in 1837.

Pairfait Dufour bought the lot in question in 1793. It was then one arpent (192 feet) square. By 1818 he had sold the northeast corner to Jean Baptiste Bossier, leaving him with an L-shaped piece of property. Dufour had a storehouse and horse mill to the south of Bossier's store.

Dufour's property could not be divided "without prejudice" according to the deed, so a public auction was held. His thirty-two-year-old son Theophilus bought both sections. A *poteaux en terre* cabin had suppos-

edly set where the Dufour House now is, but was not mentioned by the 1837 deed. The western edge of the property included "the mansion house of the deceased."

A circa 1850 painting by Conrad Roeder – interpreted and greatly enlarged in the 1990s by Janet Kraus, artist of this book's cover, the roof of what appears to be this "mansion" house is visible. After much research, diorama artist Louis Pruneau depicted the house as a large Creole house on that edge of the property. It may have stood until the 1870s. The Vogt House next door offers more likely suggestions on this topic.

The current Dufour House served as maintains several original twelve-light window sash and contributes strongly to Merchant Street's historic and aesthetic aura.

Emile Vogt House

234 Merchant

This stately 1880 brick home, nearly hidden by foliage during the spring and summer months, is interesting for more than one reason. First of all, it is a fine surviving example of a late nineteenth century T-plan house. Its exterior has not been greatly altered, with its original entrance door and its heavily molded, round-headed inset panels and arched window and door openings.

Secondly, it is interesting concerning the debate of Antoine "Parfait" Dufour and his home. Evidence today seems to indicate that the original Dufour home – built about

1793 – was built on the foundation of the Vogt house. Cellar joists and foundation appear to date back to the turn of the century or before. A May 15, 1880 *Ste. Genevieve Fair Play* article shed some light on this and on the third item of note concerning this house. "Mr. Vogt's new house will probably be commenced next week," the issue reported. "He will place a copy of this paper under the cornerstone. Probably in seventy-five or a hundred years from now – judging from the length of time the former building stood – somebody will read this notice, and wonder who Mr. Vogt was, what his business was, etc."

This tiny piece of evidence seems to support Dufour's house standing on the site of Vogt's, since the previous house on the site had stood "seventy-five to one hundred years" – for a construction date of 1780-1805. It goes on and addresses the third item of note, as well. Emile Vogt was a well loved, much respected man about town. The Fair play – for the benefit of those tearing down the house and finding the article – described him as "assessor of the county and a respected and esteemed citizen of our town." His death seventeen years later would lead to an even greater printed display of affection. (See "Papa's Not Out There Under the Snow.")

'Papa is not out there under the snow'

Emile Vogt was one of Ste. Genevieve's best-loved and most respected citizens of the late nineteenth century. Notations appeared in both the *Herald* and the *Fair Play* throughout the 1880s and 1890s in which Vogt was praised. County assessor, real estate agent and land examiner, Vogt was a community leader and a respected family man.

Aside from the fine brick house that still stands at 234 Merchant Street and the May 15, 1880 *Fair Play* issue supposedly sealed in the foundation, Vogt had another distinction in the long annals of colorful Ste. Genevieve history.

The man had one of the longest and almost certainly the most syrupy obituaries in an era when sentiment, mush, detail and poetry were quite common in the obituaries of community notables. Taking up a goodly portion of the February 13, 1897 *Herald's* front page, the obituary is one for the ages.

Vogt was hale and hearty – and, the obituary writer tells us, whether we want to know or not, still quite handsome and youthful looking in his mid fifties – until early 1896. During that year, "dialation of the stomach and tuberculosis of the bowels" set in. After a year of gut-wrenching agony, Vogt succumbed Jan. 28, 1897, at the age of fifty-four.

First of all, the obituary writer spares no detail in getting across the point that Vogt's death was a long and horrible one. "The fatal illness crept slowly upon him, but was attended with extreme suffering," it reads. "The best of local skill was employed, specialists in St. Louis were consulted. Hope was expressed, but no respite from the awful agony was obtained."

After battling what was apparently stomach cancer gamely for months, Vogt finally reached the end in late January.

"Then with lofty courage, he faced the outward journey and passed serenely into the shades of death's purple twilight." The author is not satisfied with this purple twilight, though, and while noting that Vogt had "refined tastes and that rare reverence for womanhood and courtly grace" of a southern gentleman, insists on describing the scene of his death in greater detail.

"What a pathetic sight! The devoted wife sitting through all the long agonizing hours of that last sad night holding those dear hands in hers, pale withered hands, touched even then with death's icy chill. The sorrowing son and daughters, whose idea of all that was noble was their father, gathered around the bed."

While mentioning that one daughter was on her own sick bed and that "the beseeching eyes of papa pleaded for her" in vain, the author notes that although his passing had been expected for weeks, "the blow falls piercingly as a two-edged sword, laying bare the very fibers of those loving hearts."

The writer is just getting warmed up. One wonders whether even the Vogt family – whose youngest child was already 13 – was embarrassed by the sugary prose and canned poetry.

"Visions of a barren future stretch out before their aching eyes, while memories of a happy past will crowd around them as if in mockery of the great rent and void that is in their home," he continues. "Dear hearts! Look away from the scene of parting…"

He notes that "'Papa' is well now, quite well. The torturing pain that has so wrung your own hearts will never rack him more."

After another poem, the author gears up for his grand finale in this champion of Gilded Age obituaries.

"'Papa' is not out there under the snow," it proclaims. "That is only the frail tentement, (sic) the house in which he suffered so. Would you call him back to its direful habitation? Although you miss him everywhere, would you have him feel again those mortal pains, the bursting sorrow that is in your own breasts? Ah no, no. He is at rest where we all soon shall be. The Rest of faith is supremely sweet."

So was Vogt's obituary! Vogt died within weeks of community leaders Firmin A. "General" Rozier and Charles C. "Major" Rozier as well as Emilie "Mammy" Shaw and less than four years later than Odile Pratt Valle, widow of Felix Valle, who gave three-quarters of the money to build the current Catholic church and gave the city the land for the current Valle Spring Cemetery. Yet, while the Roziers' obituaries may match Vogt's in length, no Victorian era epitaph this author has seen has equaled that of Emile Vogt in pure nineteenth century frou frou.

The author hopes the above is not offensive to readers of this work. Emile Vogt was obviously a fine family man and one of the old city's leading citizens and was no doubt fondly remembered by many. This piece merely takes a friendly poke at the mores and styles of the Gilded Age, a time when "death's icy chill," "death's purple twilight" and "Papa" not lying under the snow ccould all be squeezed into a front page obituary.

Senator Lewis F. Linn House

Officially known as the Abraham Newfield House to scholars, this early home is best known for its relatively brief association with U.S. Senator Lewis F. Linn (1795-1843). Eulogized as "Missouri's Model Senator" on his tombstone in Memorial Cemetery, Linn bought the house in 1826 and lived there at least until 1837 – if not the rest of his life.

Dr. Linn was an early and important member of the Senate. He and Missouri's senior senator, Thomas Hart Benton, formed a powerful one-two punch on issues such as the Oregon Purchase. Both were outspoken proponentsof the issue.

Born in Kentucky, Linn was a physician. He came to Ste. Genevieve in 1813 and entered the Senate in 1833, upon the death of Senator Alexander Buckner. Within a short time, the Ste. Genevieve physician had established himself as a well-liked and influential senator. Called "Father of the Platte Purchase," which expanded Missouri's original boundaries to the West, he was a friend of President Andrew Jackson and respected peer of Daniel Webster, Henry Clay, John C. Calhoun and Benton. In a 1997 paper, "Senator Lewis Fields Linn and the Platt Purchase," L. Glen Zahnd noted that "While Tom Benton had the power in the Senate, Lewis Linn had the friends." Linn's half-brother, Henry Dodge, meanwhile, was governor of the Wisconsin Territory at the time of the Platte Purchase, and was later a U.S. Senator after Wisconsin became a state.

He did not let his medical studies lag, either. During the cholera pandemic of 1833, he studied the disease and became one of the more enlightened of American doctors. In fact, it was the epidemic of 1843 that led to the good doctor's death. Leaving the capital, he hastened to Ste. Genevieve to help fight the outbreak, dying of an aneurysm under the strain.

The house was built about 1806 by Abraham Newfield, who sold the lot to Jean Ferdinand Rozier in 1820. Originally the house consisted of just the southern (street side) side of the house. Later in the century it was expanded and a center hallway was constructed in the lean-to addition. Although it was greatly altered later in the 1800s, the HABS report concluded that "the fabric of the original important early nineteenth century house survives to a remarkable degree." This includes an unadorned mantle and built-in cupboards on the second floor, as well as hand hewn sills and cellar joists.

The stone plaque bearing an 1823 date is an obvious error; this date falls well after the house's construction and before Linn's ownership of it.

Did you know?

Mary Elizabeth Rozier Sharp, queen of the gala 1935 city bicentennial, later wrote a book on the Rozier family.

S.G. Winery, Steiger Downtown

235, 242 Merchant

One of the easiest house styles to identify is the attractive, stately American Four-Square. The Ste. Genevieve Winery and Steiger Haus Downtown, built in 1908 and 1910 respectively, by two brothers, are two excellent examples.

"The cockscomb finials at the gable and dormer peaks on the ridge of the hipped roof are an unusual decorative detail not noted elsewhere in Ste. Genevieve," the HABS report notes about the winery.

A pair of brick outbuildings behind the house appear to be older than it and might have been a stable and summer kitchen. An even more important outbuilding stands behind the Steiger Haus. (See next page.)

Upstairs, above the winery is the Chateau Ste. Genevieve bed and breakfast.

Did you know?

Charles and Marjorie Bussen, who lived many years in the Bogy House, left the Bussen Estate, which helped fund the Ste. Genevieve County Community Center. Mr. Bussen owned a rock quarry north of town. In July, 1949 he discovered uranium at the quarry.

Rozier Outbuilding

242 Merchant

Jean Ferdinand Rozier came to Ste. Genevieve with John James Audubon in 1811. The former Napoleonic Navy veterans were intent on establishing themselves as successful merchants. Rozier succeeded; the Rozier Store finally closed its doors a stone's throw from this spot, in 1995. A Perryville Rozier's continues to operate. Audubon, though, proved to be more interested on ornithology and art. He left after less than a year.

Rozier bought this lot from Jacob Phillipson in 1814, after building a large frame house and a brick outbuilding here. Rozier lived there until his death in 1877. The old home was razed in May, 1880 and the current Steiger Haus Downtown eventually took its place. (See page .)

Behind this building, though, the circa 1810 brick outbuilding that seems to pre-date Rozier's ownership of the lot, still stands. The brick Anglo-American vernacular structure, was probably built by Phillipson, who owned the lot 1811-1814. Although not completely visible from the street, this is one of the most important surviving structures on Merchant Street.

"This building is the sort of utilitarian structure that does not ordinarily survive," according to the HABS report. It still has vertical sawn original rafters, ceiling boards, ceiling joists and two original twelve-light sash windows. The northern window still has its original shutters and a molded frame similar to exterior window openings of the Old Louisiana Academy. An interior door has twelve lights and is glazed. It is pegged and has through rails. Two other early beaded board-and-batten doors also survive. Made of hand-made bricks.

265 Merchant

Orris Theater

While many communities have lost their ornate, historic downtown theaters, Ste. Genevieve has been fortunate. Restored by Dick Greminger in the 1980s, the Orris, a circa 1930 commercial vernacular structure, adds much to Merchant Street. Frequented more by locals than visitors, the east side is Sirro's ("Orris" spelled backward) Restaurant, while the western side retains its theater setting. It has been the site of many school and community stage productions over the years.

The building still has its period theater marquee and its attractive mustard color bricks, "both of which contribute to its importance as an example of commercial architecture built between the World Wars," according to the HABS report.

Eagle Bakery/Nancy Dee's

252 Merchant

For many years the home of Kaegel's Country Collectibles and now Nancy Dee's Antiques, this commercial building was built as a bakery in 1908. The most interesting aspect is the stone eagle, mushrooms and the word "bakery" on a cast stone plaque above the door.

The building also preserves its original pressed metal cornice and much of its original appearance. The arched doorway near the rear of the Steiger building's east edge housed local photographer/inventor Vince Dunker's studio for many years.

Myers Shoes

289 Merchant

This small building displays most of what was outstanding in Victorian era storefront architecture. Built in1893, it has brick wall construction. The HABS reports of the 1980s said that it "presents the best-preserved commercial façade in Ste. Genevieve dating from the late nineteenth or early twentieth century."

The ornate cast iron and pressed metal ornamentation is original, intact, and meticulously maintained. The original window and door openings are still intact, as well. The ornate exterior is a reminder that the French Colonial period was not the only period of significance in Ste. Genevieve history.

Corner building

It's diagonally placed corner entrance was highly popular for corner commercial buildings at the turn of the century. It still maintains much of its original appearance. The HABS report called the flaring cornice, consoles supporting the second floor window lintels and the pedimented, projecting motif above the entryway "especially noteworthy."

Although empty at this writing, this intriguing corner building anchors the corner of Merchant and Third Streets and still provides its share of Victorian era elegance. Built during the late 1890s, it has hosted a variety of businesses over the years – usually taverns and nightclubs.

Third & Merchant

Like its sister building across Merchant Street, this corner building anchors the southeast corner of Merchant and Third Streets. It hosts Old Settlement Lights & Shades

Another of the brick commercial vernacular structures embellished with Victorian era touches, it complements the turn of the century appearance of both streets.

Its recessed corner entrance and metal support lend a touch of Victorian era elegance to the sturdy brick façade, which does not seem to have undergone many changes. A brick cornice and stone keystones and springers above the arched windows are another decorative element.

Built about 1920, this building housed Rozier' s Store 1926-1995. It is currently home to La Galerie of the French Quarter and its huge expanses upstairs have led to many discussions of possible future uses of the rest of the large structure.

The patterned brick cornice and white diamonds on the façade still make the building attractive, despite some later modifications. A 1985 mural, celebrating the town's alleged 250th anniversary that year, adds color to the downtown area. Close examination of that same eastern wall, meanwhile, seems to indicate that it might have survived from an earlier fire that gutted the previous building on that site.

Did you know?

Ste. Genevieve first celebrated its own history in July, 1885. The town marked the one hundredth anniversary of the move from the old town site in 1785 -- or the single year most associated with the move.

Although former Secretary of Interior Carl Schurz was in attendance, not everything went according to plans. It was horribly hot and humid, then a thunderstorm hit "A few minutes of the storm was sufficient to change from one of life and gaiety to a wild waste of slush and mud," the** Ste. Genevieve Herald **reported. The roof of the skating rink collapsed during the storm, although no one was hurt. One of the expected guest speakers could not be found when his speech was due and the local** La Guignolee **troop was insulted and refused to perform when its time came.

The afternoon found the heavy cloud cover back, wrapping Ste. Genevieve in a some what ominous, but comfortable shroud of gray. While the clouds seemed threatening, they also provided more relief from the summer heat.

To his servants' distress, the commandant again insisted on going out again. He had things to do and people to see – and quite possibly not long to do them and see them in. Something told him he might not be around by the time temperatures cooled off for good in the fall.

Sampson brought out the commandant's newest carriage and this time headed south down Main Street. He came to a stop at the corner of South Main and South Gabouri Streets.

"What is it?" Vallè called.

"The horse is about to throw a shoe," Sampson said. "I'd better go back and get another one."

"Very well," the commandant said, climbing out. "I'll wait here. But don't dawdle!"

While waiting on Sampson, the old man shuffled a few steps down South Gabouri and paused in front of another of the surviving colonial homes. He smiled fondly as he thought of his older brother, François Vallé II. *Look at this town now, François,* he thought. *Big, fancy buildings, more Germans moving in, the telegraph coming.*

He turned around and looked across the creek. No trace remained of the Spanish fort which had stood on the hill. The Spanish period had been a good one for the Vallés – especially after he and François had won a protracted power battle with Commandant Henri Peyroux. He smiled at the thoughts of the battles François and Peyroux had waged.

He headed back to the intersection when he heard the carriage returning. After getting back in, he gazed at Julien LaBruyere's former home, perched atop the precipice by the creek. He and his father, Louis Ratte LaBruyere, had been fine people. He chuckled at the site of Moses Austin's former outbuilding. None of the French had been overly trusting of the Yankee entrepreneur when he had come to town in the 1790s, but he had certainly revolutionized lead mining in the region. That, in turn, had made them all money.

He signaled for Sampson to stop at Ziegler' s tobacco shop. Shaking his head and obviously sighing, Sampson pulled over alongside the large, sleek building.

"I have some fond memories of this place, Sampson," he confided, after Zeke had helped him from the buggy. "Back when Monsieur Janis owned it, we would hold dances upstairs. It was quite festive."

Sampson tried to picture the commandant and the late Mrs. Vallé dancing in time to a fiddle player, but was unable to. "I remember the 'Green Tree Tavern' sign hanging there,' he said.

"Yes, it was a good place to stay, as well as being a tavern and dance hall. And now, of course, it's the best place in town to get tobacco!"

After shooting the bull for several minutes with proprietor Mathias Ziegler, they both returned to the carriage.

"Colonel Vallé, your patronage is always appreciated," Ziegler said in his rough French.

"Why send to New Orleans when we have fine snuff and tobacco right here?" the commandant replied with a smile. "Of course I made many trips on a keelboat or raft, bringing tobacco and coffee back from there!"

"It was a different world, was it not?" Ziegler exclaimed. "The riverboat changed everything."

"Very much so," the commandant agreed, climbing back into the carriage. "That and the telegraph and this railroad. Why, I could take a boat to St. Louis today, get on one of those trains and be in Washington or New York before I knew it!"

He leaned over and gave Ziegler a conspiratory wink.

"And if I were ten years younger, I'd be tempted to try it!"

"Would you visit Europe if you were younger, Colonel?"

"Oh, I don't know about *that!*" Vallé replied. "All these revolutions! Why, half of Europe was up in arms last summer – though apparently it's all petered out since. I've managed to miss every revolution during the last ninety years and I've no mind to jump into one today! Of course I was madder than a hornet when Papa wouldn't let me go with the militia unit to defend St. Louis back in eighty. Both of my brothers went, but Papa didn't want to risk losing all three heirs."

"That is understandable," Ziegler replied. "But I'm sure you wanted to go, fight."

"I felt cheated at the time," the commandant said, leaning on his cane. "I had been in the militia since I was fourteen. But I'm sure it was God's providence that kept me out of it."

"And his providence that has allowed many of my countrymen to come to America since last summer," the German added. "Have you noticed?"

"I've noticed the Germans continuing to flock in!" Valle said with a wink. "A bunch of tidy beer-drinking, brick-laying Protestants!"

The two men shared a hardy chuckle.

"It is good to see you up and about," Ziegler said a moment later. "I must get back to work. Please stop in again soon!"

After waving to Ziegler, the commandant rode past the Misplait house, then waved at Augustine St. Gemme, who was standing in front of his house, further down the road that used to go to New Bourbon. He signaled for Sampson to pull over when he saw Clarise Ribault in front of her home.

"Good afternoon, my dear!" he cried, admiring the large garden beside the small house. "What a nice job you have done with the grounds and garden."

"Thank you, Colonel Vallé," said the attractive, sturdily-built black woman as she stepped to the carriage. Like Emilie Shaw, she was also a recent widow. "You are looking well."

"Thank you, dear," he said, "As are you. It is so much nicer today, I decided to get out and take a good look around town."

"It seems everyone is out and about today," she answered. "That Roeder boy has been running around, sketching drawings of different houses."

"Yes, he said something about painting a view of the entire town," Vallè answered.

"I suppose no one will bother painting or drawing in a few years," Clarise replied, wiping sweat from her brow. "I hear they have these … cameras?"

"Yes, cameras," he reassured her.

"They have these cameras that can take a daguerreotype of a person or a building," she continued. "Have you seen one?"

"*Seen* one? I've *posed* for one!" he replied with a chuckle. "But what a horrific result! I look like death warmed over."

He paused and chuckled.

"Of course the camera lens does not lie," he added. "A sympathetic painter can make one look much younger. The camera will not give one the same courtesy."

He added as an after thought. "If you would like to see it, come over sometime. But I warn you, it's not a pretty sight!"

After continuing his ride, the commandant rode past Pierre Dorlac's old house, which one of his own sons had also owned, and on to the former town of New Bourbon. He looked sadly at the virtually abandoned streets where French and American immigrants had built a successful community some sixty years before. He looked nostalgically across *le Grand Champ*. The old town site had been gone for years, too.

The commandant sighed as Sampson turned the buggy and began the trot back into town. *Toward the cemetery,* he thought. *I suppose it's about time.*

S. Gabouri-St. Marys Rd. Map

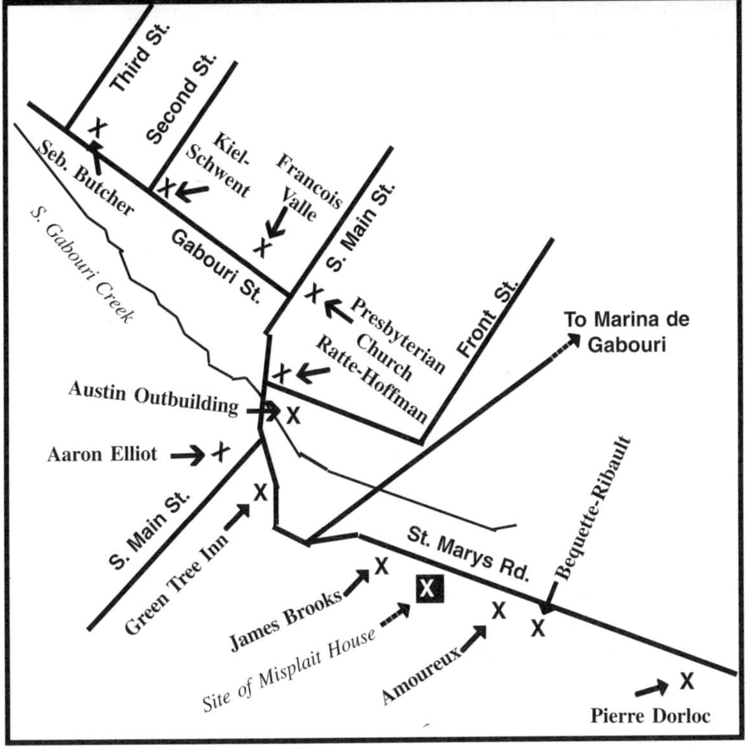

Third St.
Second St.
Kiel-Schwent
Francois Valle
S. Main St.
Seb. Butcher
Gabouri St.
S. Gabouri Creek
Presbyterian Church
Ratte-Hoffman
Front St.
To Marina de Gabouri
Austin Outbuilding
Aaron Elliot
S. Main St.
Green Tree Inn
St. Marys Rd.
Bequette-Ribault
James Brooks
Site of Misplait House
Amoureux
Pierre Dorloc

Kiel-Schwent House

198 N. Second

Formerly known as the François Vallé Stone House, this attractive little building was actually constructed some ten years after the commandant's death.

Built about 1814 by Henry Kiel (See Dufour Stone Building, page 33), the ashlar limestone building is now home to The Foundation for Restoration of Ste. Genevieve, Inc. It was donated by the Schwent family in 1994, along with funds to help restore it. In houses a conference room, offices and sleeping rooms for official visitors and contains archival materials and The Mecker Book Collection. The Foundation office is open much of the week.

It has been greatly altered over the years. Like the John Birke House (See page 102), it was probably originally a one-story hall-and-parlor house. Most of the interior woodwork comes from a later period, although some original vertical sawn ceiling joists are visible in the attic.

Sebastian Butcher House

Thought to have been built of braced heavy timber frame construction throughout at the time of the HABS reports of the 1980s, the western half of this house – not visible at that time – has since proven to be built of vertical logs.

Built between 1818 and 1821 by Sebastian Butcher, the house seems to give some evidence that the original part may have been a one-room cabin. Although no break seems to appear in the foundation walls, the joists in the eastern half are square hewn and those in the western half are puncheons. Braced, heavy timber frame construction with mortised and pegged uprights are visible in the eastern part of the cellar.

Did you know?

Ste. Genevieve was named for Genevieve, the fifth-century patron saint of Paris, who helped the city repel Atilla the Hun by calling for city-wide prayer and fasting.

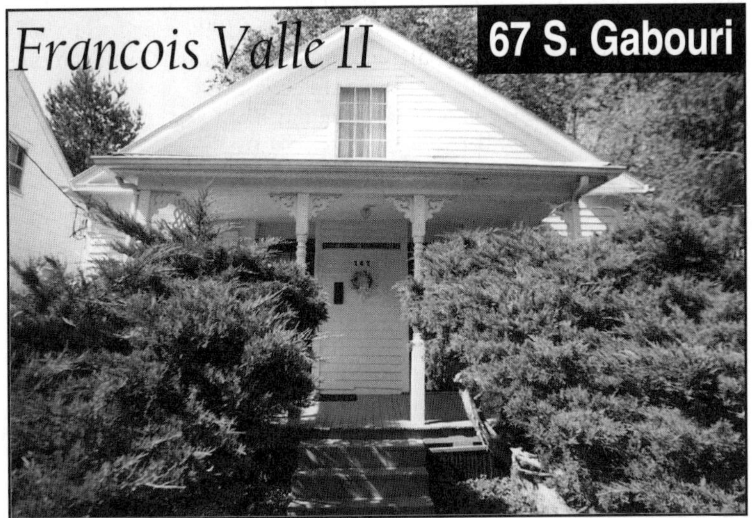

Another of the French Creole homes that bears maintains little of its original fabric – at least visible fabric, this attractive frame house is significant for its first occupant and the importance of his move into that home.

When François Vallé II moved from the old town site to the new – probably in 1792, it helped mark the death knell for the old community. The move to *les petite côtes* had been going on for several years. When influential citizens like Vallé and Louis Bolduc built homes in the new town, it was the beginning of the end for the old town.

The house has always been the center of some debate. The vertical log structure appears to have been just twenty-seven by twenty-six feet – hardly the size home one would expect a man with his eyes on the commandant's position. (He got that title in 1794 after winning a protracted battle of wills with the aloof Henri Peyroux.) According to the HABS reports, it "probably represents a portion of the large house that belonged to him or is an outbuilding attendant to the now vanished larger house."

Despite this idea, though, no evidence has ever surfaced to prove the existence of a larger house somewhere on his property – that ran along South Gabouri Street, from South Main to Third Street. Vallé, whose wife was said to dress somewhat in a Native American style, may simply have been content with a house much smaller than some of his compatriots.

Did you know?

Jour de Fete, originated in the late 1960s, draws several times the population of Ste. Genevieve to town each August.

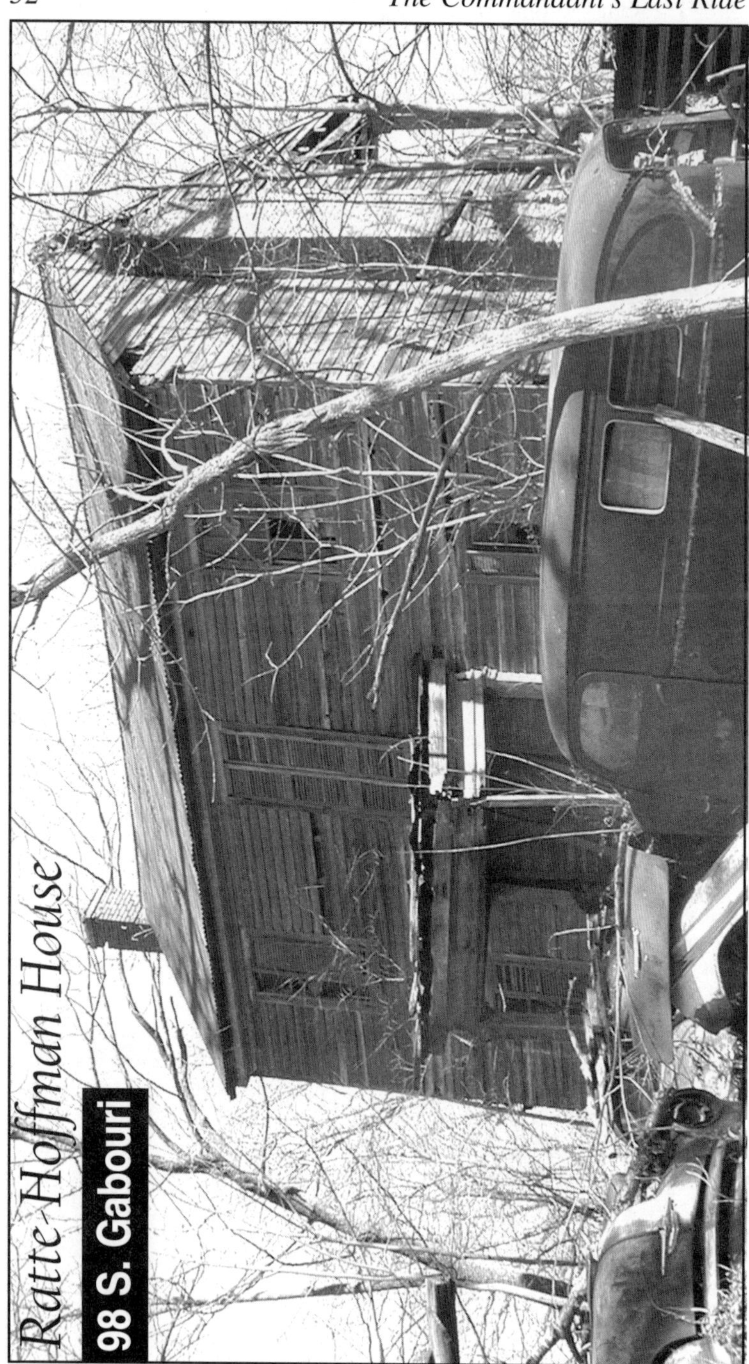
Ratte-Hoffman House
98 S. Gabouri

The Ratte-Hoffman House has always been a house of extremes. It is doubtful that Ste. Genevieve boasted a more attractive house and grounds during the first decades of the nineteenth century.

During the second half of the twentieth century the old home became truly spectacular in its deterioration. It equally drew the ire of some preservationists and tidy German neighbors and the enthusiasm of photographers and artists.

It was the spectacular ruin towering above the South Gabouri Creek, lined in a perfect circle by rusted automobiles of various eras, that this writer told his friends about after his first adult visit to Ste. Genevieve in 1986. The old Federal I-house, dark gray from a lack of paint, was the perfect focal point of the car carcasses that surrounded it. There was something so poetic about the site – especially prior to the floods of the 1990s that marred some of the symmetry – that defies easy description.

Now a new chapter is being written on the historic home. Possibly the most ambitious restoration project in Ste. Genevieve is being planned for the Ratte-Hoffman. The fourth generation of the Hoffman family is determined to save the house and restore it to its old grandeur.

Dr. Osmund Overby, head of

The Hoffman family recently unearthed this ca. 1930 photo of the house -- the earliest known shot of the building.

the Historic American Buildings Survey (HABS) during the 1980s, has called it "one of the finest remaining American houses from the early nineteenth century."

"Perhaps because this house has been allowed to deteriorate instead of being expanded and modernized over the years, its present appearance is close to that of the original building," he suggested, noting that it appears to be one of the few early Ste. Genevieve houses with a central hall way.

Believed to have been built in 1809, after locksmith Louis Ratte LaBruyere left the property to his son Julien, this three-bay frame I-house with brick end chimneys and two-story rear porch is of heavy-timber frame construction.

It was purchased by John McArthur and also owned by John Scott, Missouri's first U.S. Representative. The house was supposedly a stage coach stop during the mid nineteenth century and was later the home of Dr. Francis J. Bennays. It was later owned by the Burch family.

Glory Days

Diorama artist Lewis Pruneau came up with this depiction of the old home in 1832. Its gardens, lush lawn and towering view of the South Gabouri Creek no doubt made it an ideal home.

Moses Austin Outbuilding

78 N. Main

Connecticut Yankee Moses Austin was a huge figure in Missouri – as well as Texas – history. Austin arrived in Missouri in 1797 and within a few years thoroughly modernized and revolutionized Missouri lead mining.

Although his primary residence was Durham Hall in Potosi (which burned in 1871), he also had a substantial house next door to the Ratte-Hoffman House. Two buildings purported to have been Austin outbuildings still stand nearby. The building pictured is believed to have been built as a detached kitchen for the former Austin house. The southeast and east portion appear to be original to that time period. Later in the century the front of the current structure was added, with its pedimented door and window heads and dormers, indicating Greek Revival influence.

Austin, after going bankrupt in an 1818 bank failure, had just made arrangements to take a group of settlers from Potosi to the frontier of what would become Texas, when he died in 1823. His son Stephen F. Austin followed in Moses' footsteps and led the original "Old 300" settlers to Texas and to immortality. Austin is buried in Potosi.

The house, now owned by the Jour de Fete Committee, has a second reason for significance. In 1840 it passed into owner ship of a "free woman of color," who had been Austin's slave at one time. It, the Bequette-Ribault, and the Becka Hunt House in Commerce, may be the only surviving homes in Missouri, owned by free black women prior to the Civil War.

Aaron Elliott/Annie's B & B

This attractive shingled home, nestled between the Green Tree Inn and the South Gabouri Creek, is the oldest surviving frame house in town that was built by an Anglo-American. The original part of the house (facing Seraphin Street) dates to the 1806-1812 period.

Now home of Annie's B & B, the old home – said to have been an early Ste. Genevieve Post Office and home of Dr. Aaron Elliot – maintains much of its original fabric. The plates, sills and principal uprights are hand hewn in the original portion, while corner braces and intermediate uprights are vertical sawn. Likewise, some cellar joists are vertical sawn and some hand-hewn. Most of the woodwork in the house seems to come form the mid nineteenth century.

The HBAS report points out that the roof frame "differs from those of other early nineteenth century structures built by Americans or influenced by American construction practices... since its vertical sawn coupled rafters are not braced by collar beams."

Did you know?

President Franklin D. Roosevelt spoke to Ste. Genevieve residents in August, 1935, during the city's Bicentennial. A special $400 line was installed to allow the President to speak through the phone, over a loud speaker. Rep. Clyde Williams and the Rev. J.B. Platisha, Bicentennial Pageant director, attended a White House press conference in July, inviting the President and First Lady to attend.

Janis-Zieglar/
GreenTree Tavern
241 St. Marys Rd.

One of the most time-honored oral traditions in Ste. Genevieve was that François Janis constructing a hollow area in his home's great triangular fireplace, to hide the women and children of the family during Indian attacks.

Had the Osage Indians decided to attack the house in the 1790s, however, the Janis children would have been on their own. Contrary to legend, there was no secret hiding place in the fireplace after all.

This is just one of the time-honored myths owner Hilliard J. Goldman has been able to shatter during his extensive restoration of the Janis-Ziegler House – known locally as the Green Tree Tavern. Finding interior bricks in the huge fireplace crumbling, Goldman and architect Jack Luer had to dig deep inside the chimney pillar early in the building's restoration, removing bad bricks. The results answered age-old speculation.

"You can see right from one room into the other room," Goldman said. "There is no hiding place inside."

The oldest building in Missouri, according to tree ring dating, the Green Tree was built in 1790 and 1791 by Francois Janis or his father, Nicolas. It is framed with sturdy white oak timbers and maintains much of its original black walnut trim and walnut shutters. Some of the original pine flooring also survives in part of the house. Whitewash was still visible over the vertical oak logs and bouzillage when lathing was torn away during the restoration. While it predates any of Ste. Genevieve's purely Creole buildings, the great house, with more than 2,000-square-feet of first floor space, is a transitional one. Goldman believes it had its end gables and American style truss from the very beginning and that the northwest corner was originally enclosed.

Through intense inspection and architectural detective work, the house has yielded other answers, as well. Local lore has always said that the Green Tree became the first tavern in U.S. territory west of the Mississippi in 1804 and later the first tobacco store in that region.

Goldman is convinced that Janis opened the tavern immediately upon construction of the house, rather than after the Louisiana Purchase. He believes the tavern was in one of the first floor rooms – with outside tables certainly being available on the *galerie* during good weather. It was in this room, meanwhile, that evidence points to as the Masonic meeting room. He believes they have also identified the room used for inn guests and another (on the far southwest corner) which was the scullery. In 1860 a wall and second triangular fireplace were removed, making one large dining room.

Guests did not sleep in the attic, Goldman and Luer believe. They did gather there to dance and party, though. Janis was known to be a fiddle player and Goldman makes a convincing case that the great open space under the trusses (with well over six feet of clearance) was built with a ball room in mind.

Thanks to the difficulty in removing the huge fireplaces in the east end of the house, the Green Tree escaped the fate of many early Ste. Genevieve houses during the nineteenth century wave of "Americanization." Much of the floor plan and fabric remain from the eighteenth century. Noted architectural historian Osmund Overby has said that the house "contains the most unaltered interior of any surviving French vertical log house in Ste. Genevieve."

The old building was restored by Frankye and Norbert Donze in the 1970s and opened as a tourist attraction. The 1993 flood led the city to elevate St. Marys Road, thus covering the 1803 retaining wall which gave the Green Tree part of its unique historic charm. Goldman has challenged the city to restore the street to its original level, so that the retaining wall and rock steps may be restored.

The grand house sat for some two months in flood waters in 1993.

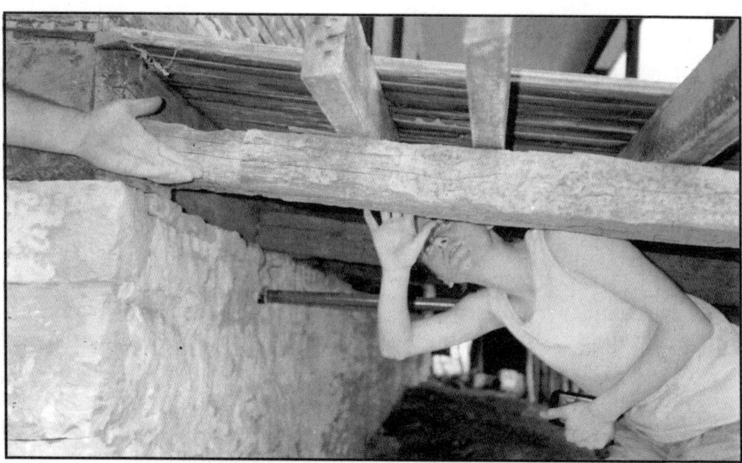

A Southeast Missouri State University historic preservation student checks out an original Green Tree Inn beam.

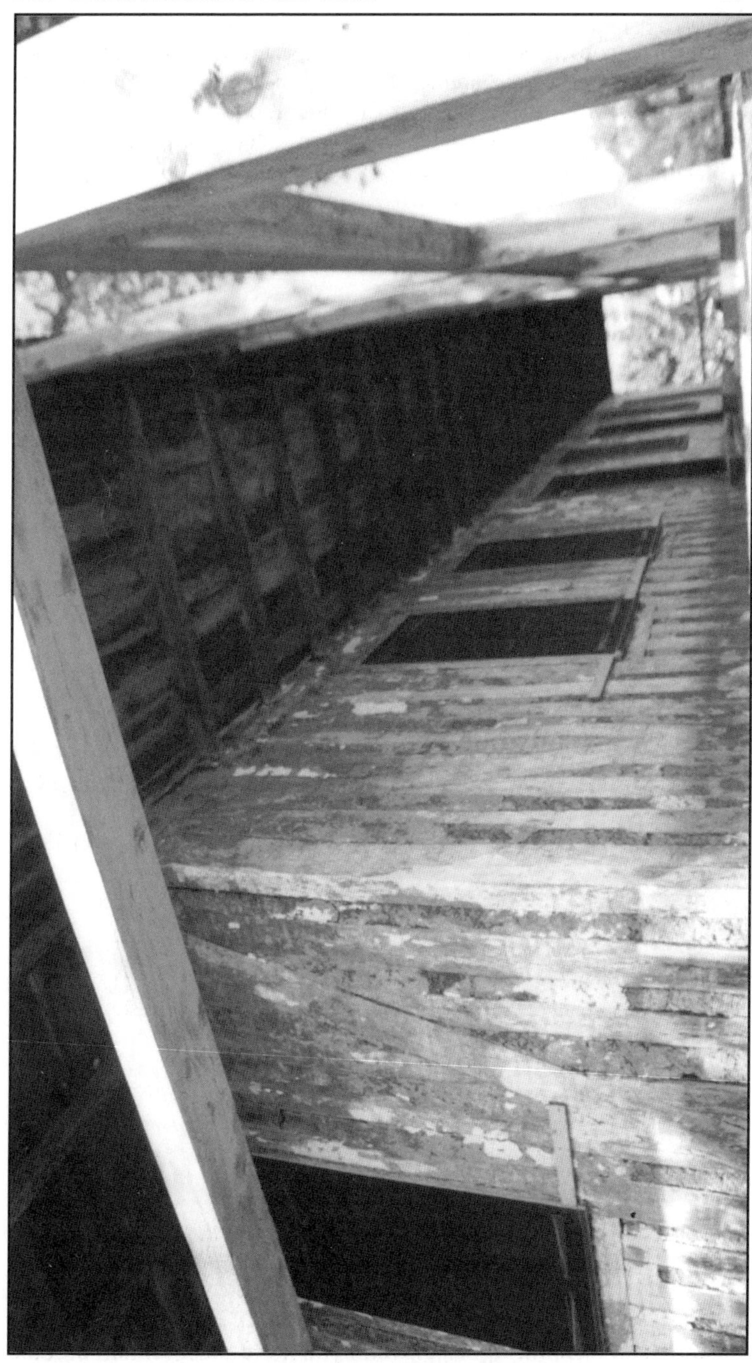

Water was eighteen inches deep inside the house. It was on the cover of *Damaged and Threatened National Historic Landmarks 1993 Report,* a National Park Service publication of endangered places. While the *galerie* has had to be totally reconstructed, Goldman and Luer have been able to save much of the house's original fabric. A second triangular chimney and staircase – both removed in 1860 – have been reconstructed, using all the clues available. All wood used as replacement pieces or for reconstruction were cut with an adz by Jesse Francis, curator of St. Louis County's historic buildings at Faust Park. They have also replaced the removed walls, giving the house its original number of rooms.

The best bet on the reproduced triangular chimney was that it had contained a French beehive bake oven. Three other such ovens exist in Ste. Genevieve houses from the period and the clues Luer uncovered all seem to fit. So do those concerning the reconstructed 1790 staircase, which Goldman is confident matches the original.

"It's a reconstruction, but not speculation," Goldman said of the stairway. "If Mr. Janis came back, he would recognize it. We're not doing anything that we cannot justify . Where there's speculation, we let you know."

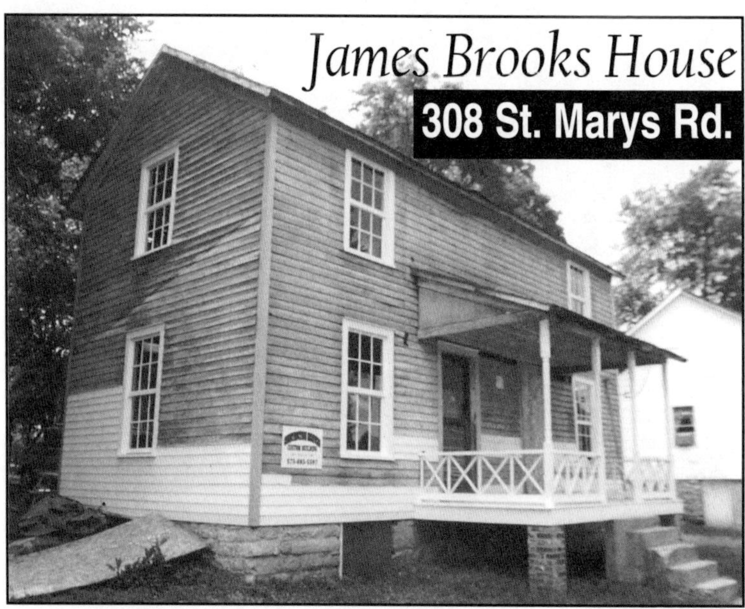
James Brooks House
308 St. Marys Rd.

Ste. Genevieve nearly lost its last remaining link to the purely African-American families of its past. Sitting neglected and flood-ravaged for nearly fifteen years, the William Brooks House was threatened with demolition before local preservationists were able to convince Brooks' heirs that the house was worth restoring.

The dilapidated kitchen wing has been removed from the James Brooks House.

Built in 1861 according to dendrochronology, the one and a half story frame I-house was home to William Brooks, probably the most respected and esteemed black resident Ste. Genevieve ever had. Brooks (1889-1984) was a domestic servant for the Henry L. Rozier (Sr. and Jr.) families and later for Anne Valle. Brooks Drive on the western end of town bears his name. A World War I veteran, he married Johannah McNabb, the teacher at Lincoln School, Ste. Genevieve's school for African-Americans during the days of segregation. Johannah McNabb Brooks was a brilliant woman, who went on to earn her master' s degree and was a professor at Stowe Teachers College (now Harris-Stowe University) in St. Louis, when she was killed in a car wreck at age thirty-seven in 1942.

Brooks was left to bring up three young sons. He did so with flying colors, with all three sons forging successful careers. Son William, Jr., in fact, was running for mayor of Detroit at the time of this printing.

Brooks lived to be ninety-four and residents who knew him say he was the last "gentleman" in town who tipped his hat to women in the street. Another son, Jack, broke the color barrier at both local high schools, attending Valle Catholic High School briefly, then Ste. Genevieve High School, as a senior in 1954-55.

The house, covered with Virginia creeper, had been inundated by the 1993 flood and had sat empty since Brooks' death in 1984. It was considered significant because it and the well-maintained house next door are the only surviving examples of the double pen I-houses typical of African-American construction of the period. Black families traditionally lived in "clusters" of two to four houses in Ste. Genevieve.

Contractor Jim Beckerman is restoring the old home, which will serve as a cultural heritage museum. The collapsed circa 1940 kitchen ell was removed when restoration work began.

St. Gemme/Amoureux House

Called by some the most primitive of Ste. Genevieve's historic houses, the Amoureux House was built about 1792 and is one of three *poteaux en terre* houses in Ste. Genevieve. (As related on the next page, only five survive in the United States.)

The roof system consists of king-post trusses and wind braces. Experts believe the roof profile was changed in the nineteenth century from a hipped roof of thatch to the current gabled roof. It almost certainly was built without *galeries*. Originally the building extended several feet farther to the West. Currently a gift shop – built in the 1960s when the Amoureux was a museum house – sits there now. Plans call for the gift shop's eventual demolition.

The board-and-batten cellar doors and their hand-wrought hardware may be original. Entering the cellar gives one a face-to-face encounter with the 200-year-old red cedar logs. This can be a momentous experience, considering all these vertical logs have withstood.

The Amoureux is now the property of the Missouri Department of Natural Resources. The DNR staff has been working in recent years to take the old home back as closely as feasible to its 1790s appearance.

The Amoureux has pine flooring today, but Dr. Richard Guyette of the University of Missouri believes the original floors were walnut. Old walnut boards were found lying in the basement dirt and being used as shims during the HABS studies of the 1980s. The boards had grooves on each side, for a spline.

Built by Jean Baptiste St. Gemme Beauvais, it was bought by Benjamin Amoureux in 1852 and remained in the Amoureux family for generations. It was not, however, owned by Michel Mathurin Amoureux, a French nobleman and correspondent of Thomas Jefferson, who came to Ste. Genevieve in 1793. This was among the many inaccurate local legends about the old house. Rumors of it being disassembled and moved from the old village after the 1785 flood are also discredited today.

It stayed in the Amoureux family well into the twentieth century. Restored by Norbert and Frankye Donze in the 1960s, it was one of the town's early tour houses. At one time it was well known for its huge doll collection.

The Amoureux survived the summer of 1993, in which flood water filled its basement, soaking those centuries-old posts. They needed bracing afterward, but none of the historic fabric of the house was lost due to the flood. Again open to the public, it today hosts Lewis Pruneau's spectacular circa 1832 diorama of Ste. Genevieve – funded by Les Amis.

The 'other two' of the five

The Amoureux House is one of three *poteaux en terre* structures in Ste. Genevieve and one of just five known surviving examples in the United States.

One, the Badin-Roque House, was built near Natchitoches, LA about 1770 as a private residence. It was used as a convent during the mid nineteenth century before becoming a residence again.

Built with vertical cypress logs and infilled with *bouzillage*, it has a dirt floor. In 1979 the St. Augustine Historical Society purchased the house from Zeline Badin Roque's heirs. The only surviving example of *poteaux en terre* and *bouzillage* architecture in Louisiana, it has been placed on the National Register of Historic Places. Now a fixture in central Louisiana tourism, it is site of the annual Creole Heritage Day celebration each January.

Considered the oldest building between the Alleghenies and the Rockies, the La Pointe-Krebs House in Pascagoula, MS was supposedly built in 1726. Numerous historical and archaeological studies during the past quarter century have neither been able to prove nor disprove the traditional construction date. It appears likely, though, that the original structure – built as a tool shed or carpentry shop on the Joseph Simon de La Pointe Plantation – was either badly damaged or destroyed in a 1772 hurricane.

The plantation was later owned by La Pointe's son-in-law, Hugo Ernestus Krebs, who was said to have invented a cotton gin many years before Eli Whitney.

Studies have revealed that the original building was expanded twice and that openings were cut into walls at a later date to allow for the construction of fireplaces. It was also built with cyprus logs and *bouzillage* and had an oyster shell concrete floor from the very beginning. A wooden floor was later placed over the concrete. Known locally as "The Old Spanish Fort," even though it never served as such, it was in the Krebs family until 1914. In 1940 Jackson County, MS bought it and stabilized the crumbling building. In 1996 an extensive restoration was performed, returning it to a circa 1820 appearance. It is open to the public.

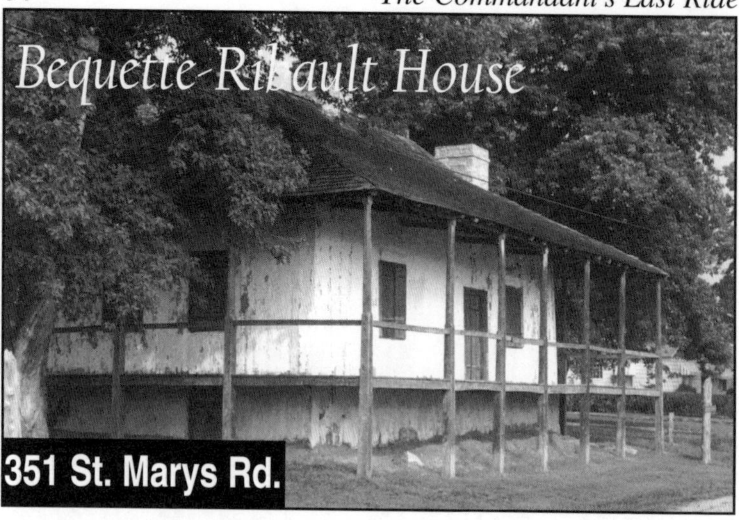

Few houses look more innocent than the charmingly restored Bequette-Ribault House. Yet no house in Ste. Genevieve – or Missouri, for that matter – has caused as much controversy and debate.

Dr. Richard Guyette performed the first tree ring test on a Missouri house when he tested the Bequette-Ribault in 1984.

The *poteaux en terre* home was long believed to have been built by the 1770s or 1780s. Dendrochronology tests in 1984, however, pointed to an 1807-1808 construction date. Some observers, such as architect Jack Luer who led the restoration of the house, have never accepted the later dates.

Despite the controversy, the old home is imminently important. For one, it is one of the five known surviving *poteaux en terre* buildings in the United States. For another, it is one of only two known houses in Missouri which were owned by a free black woman prior to the Civil War.

Jean Baptiste Bequette owned the lot in the late 1700s and either he or his descendents built the house. In 1837 it was sold to Clarise, "a free woman of color," from Virginia. She lived with – and may or may not have been married to – a well to do French widower named John Ribault. She bore him two sons and the house passed on to the next generation in 1869.

Old Ste. Genevieve was largely color blind and "mulatto" children of white and black or white and Indian parents did not seem to face discrimination here during colonial days or in the early nineteenth century.

The Ribaults continued to occupy the house until the Clarise's last grandson died in 1969. By 1980, the abandoned house was on its last legs. Royce and Marge Wilhauk pur-

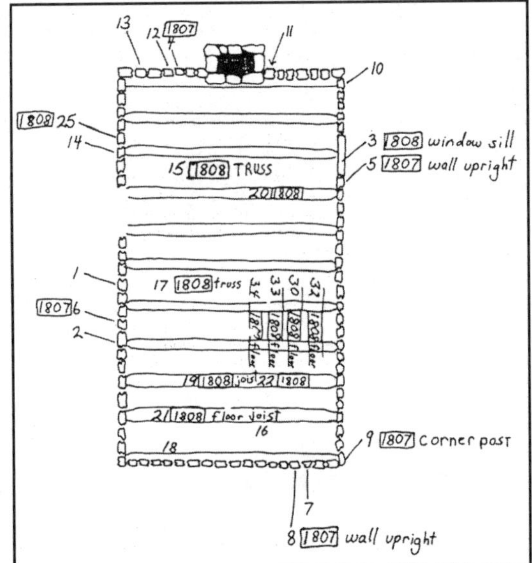

Guyette's thorough 1984 tree ring tests on the Bequette-Ribault (above) produced 1807-1808 dates with both red cedar and white oak, as well as shortleaf pine. Below, the intriguing little home as it looked around the turn of the century. It stayed in the Ribault family for 162 years.

chased it and had a painstaking restoration done on it in the mid 1980s, led by Jack Luer, Jesse Francis and archaeologist Mel Thurman. It was during the restoration that Dr. Richard Guyette's tree ring tests were done.

When the initial tests came back with 1807 and 1808 dates, Guyette returned and did more. All together, he made twenty-one borings in the house. All came back with 1807 and 1808 dates. This included eleven red cedar wall logs (1807), seven white oak boards (1808) and four short pine floor boards (1808). Some argue that red cedar is nearly impossible to date. Guyette, though, only used pieces that he could cross-match. Of course the white oak, which critics agree dates easily, produced the same result.

Privately owned, the home is occasionally open to the public

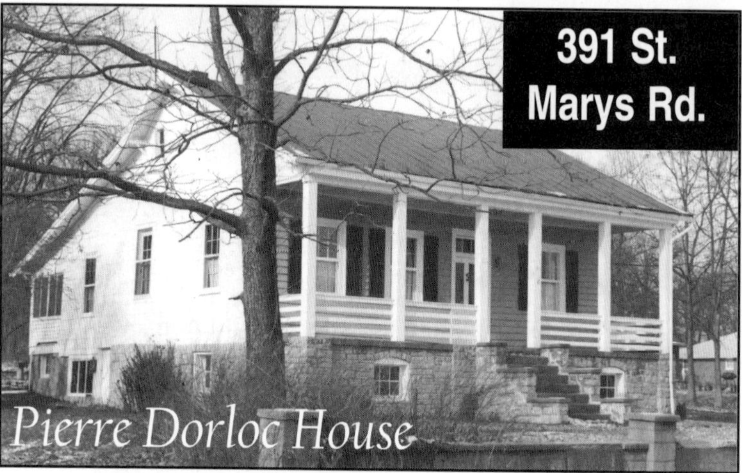

Modern science has given an interesting glimpse into the construction of the attractive Pierre Dorlac House. It was not uncommon for lumber to be latched together and floated downriver as makeshift rafts, before being cut to size. This, it appears, was the case with this small house.

Dr. Richard Guyette discovered what appeared to be mineralization marks on the white oak beams, indicating likely water transport to Ste. Genevieve. The house dates to 1806 or 1807 and – like the Green Tree Inn – is a transitional house, showing American and Creole building practices coexisting. Owned at one time by Jean Baptiste Valle II, the French Creole vernacular structure is built of closely-spaced hand-hewn white oak posts, mortised to plates and sills. The rafters are vertical sawn and are braced by white oak collar beams.

Shortleaf pine ceiling joists are still visible on the porch, despite the house's remodeling to a Greek Revival look later in the nineteenth century. The Central hallway and pedimented door and window lintels were apparently added at that time.

The commandant signaled for Sampson to turn left onto Market Street instead of stopping in front of the house. As the carriage passed the LaPorte house and neared Third Street, he motioned to the left. Sampson pulled up in front of an imposing two and a half story brick structure. A sign proclaimed "Kern's Hotel." He helped the commandant down from the carriage.

"May as well step in and see who's in the tavern, Sampson," he explained. "I haven't seen many people recently."

He made his way into the tavern, where he enjoyed a quick drink, then visited with some of the young men shooting pool. He regaled them with tales of the building's original owner, John Donohue, and his destructive habit of betting on billiards. Returning to the buggy, he found Sampson missing. *I know where he is,* the old man thought with a smile, walking around the carriage and toward the livery stable across from the hotel.

"Ready to go already, Commandant?" Sampson gasped when Vallé stepped into the building.

"Just how much drinking did you expect me to *do?"* he asked with mock exasperation. "Do you think I'm becoming a lush in my old age?"

Sampson chuckled and apologized for keeping him waiting as they returned to the carriage. He also passed along the name of a county farmer who was expecting a batch of top quality ponies in a few days. The commandant was about to reply when the church bell began peeling. He checked his pocket watch.

"I think I'll go to mass while I'm out and about," he said. *I may not have many more chances.*

As Sampson passed the old John Price building, the commandant thought back to the days when the fine building was the site of the first U.S. district court in the county. Like Donohue, old Price had had trouble hanging onto his possessions, too. The building had been auctioned off later on, to pay debts. Sampson let the old gentleman off in front of the ornate cut stone church. Odile Valle was standing on the steps, conversing with a nun when he arrived. She quickly went to him and helped him up the steps.

"Colonel Vallé, so nice to see you at Mass," Father St. Cyr beamed afterward. "I had planned on visiting you later this week."

"Not for last rights, I hope!" the commandant quipped.

"Oh, no, certainly not!" the new priest exclaimed. "In fact, you're looking fit and well, today."

"More so than I have lately," he reluctantly agreed. He looked skyward at the sound of distant thunder. "Will we get more rain?"

"We had prayed for it long enough, Colonel," the priest replied, also looking into the cloudy sky. "I hope we get a bit more."

"Maybe I had better do some walking before we have a foot of mud in the streets," Vallé said. He called to Sampson and told him he would walk around the block.

Accompanied by his daughter-in-law, Vallé stepped onto Fourth Street and pointed to a Creole house across the street.

"You're probably too young to remember Charles Gregoire," he said. "He was a fine man. So was Jacque Guibourd."

He nodded at the Guibourd house, where two children were playing in the yard.

"I remember when Omer Guibourd made his first visit to France," she said, "and met General LaFayette on the way."

"Oh, yes!" the old man recalled fondly. "Lucky him! Imagine, him going down the river just as the general was coming up."

"Did he stop here?"

"Very briefly. He didn't use that carriage Omer talked about."

"With the six white horses."

"Or so Omer said."

They both chuckled as they continued down the block, past the old Pratte Warehouse and the towering new convent.

"The sisters seem to like their new home," Odile said.

"Can you blame them?" he asked, glancing up at the imposing brick structure. "They certainly have plenty of room here."

"We've been so fortunate to have the Sisters of Loretto here," she said.

"Yes indeed," the commandant replied. "Did you know that the founder of their order died right here in Ste. Genevieve?"

"He *did?*" she gasped.

"Why yes," he answered. " Father Nerinckx stopped here on his way back from St. Louis, some years before the sisters came here, and was taken ill. He died in the old rectory that used to stand right over there."

"Is this far enough?" she asked in a minute, as they reached the corner of Fourth and Jefferson. He nodded, but pointed to the attractive stone house across the street.

"Jean Baptiste Hubardeau built that house some thirty years ago," he said. "I know his dad was way before your time, but he was quite a character. Old Simon Hubardeau. He was a smart man, but always seemed to be getting himself into trouble!"

As they made their way back to the church yard, he related favorite exploits of Hubardeau.

By the time he reached the carriage, the commandant had had enough activity for one day. He hoped it might be pleasant enough to get out and about the next day as well. There was still much of the old town he hadn't seen in weeks.

See page 91 for a map of this section and the west-central part of town, including The Old Louisiana Academy and Memorial Cemetery, as well as Third and Fourth Streets.

Church of Ste. Genevieve

When the Church of Ste. Genevieve was constructed and consecrated on this lot in 1794, it officially marked the death of the old town site by the river. The church and the Spanish garrison of soldiers were probably the last vestiges of the old town to make the move.

Local stories that the church was disassembled and moved from the old town seem to be ludicrous. In a letter to Governor-General Carondelet in 1792, the Abbe de St. Pierre, mentions "a propped up church, an old rectory, [and] miserable quarters for seven and one-half soldiers" being all that remained in the old town. If the church in the old town was falling apart by the time of the move, it seems unlikely that any components were even salvaged.

A new wooden church was constructed at that time, after Zenon Trudeau, governor-general of Upper Louisiana, finally visited to work out disagreements on how much various individuals would be expected to give toward the construction – more evidence of fresh construction on the site.

In 1823, Father Charles Nerninckx, founder of the Sisters of Loretto – who would later put in some twenty years of good work in the town – died in Ste. Genevieve. Taken ill on a return trip from St. Louis, he apparently died in the old rectory, after receiving last rights from the pastor, Father Xavier Dahmen. Bishop Joseph Rosati, informed of Nerninckx's illness, arrived a day later and escorted the body back to Kentucky for burial.

On the following pages are two views taken fromThird Street, looking toward the church. The first was during the 1870s.

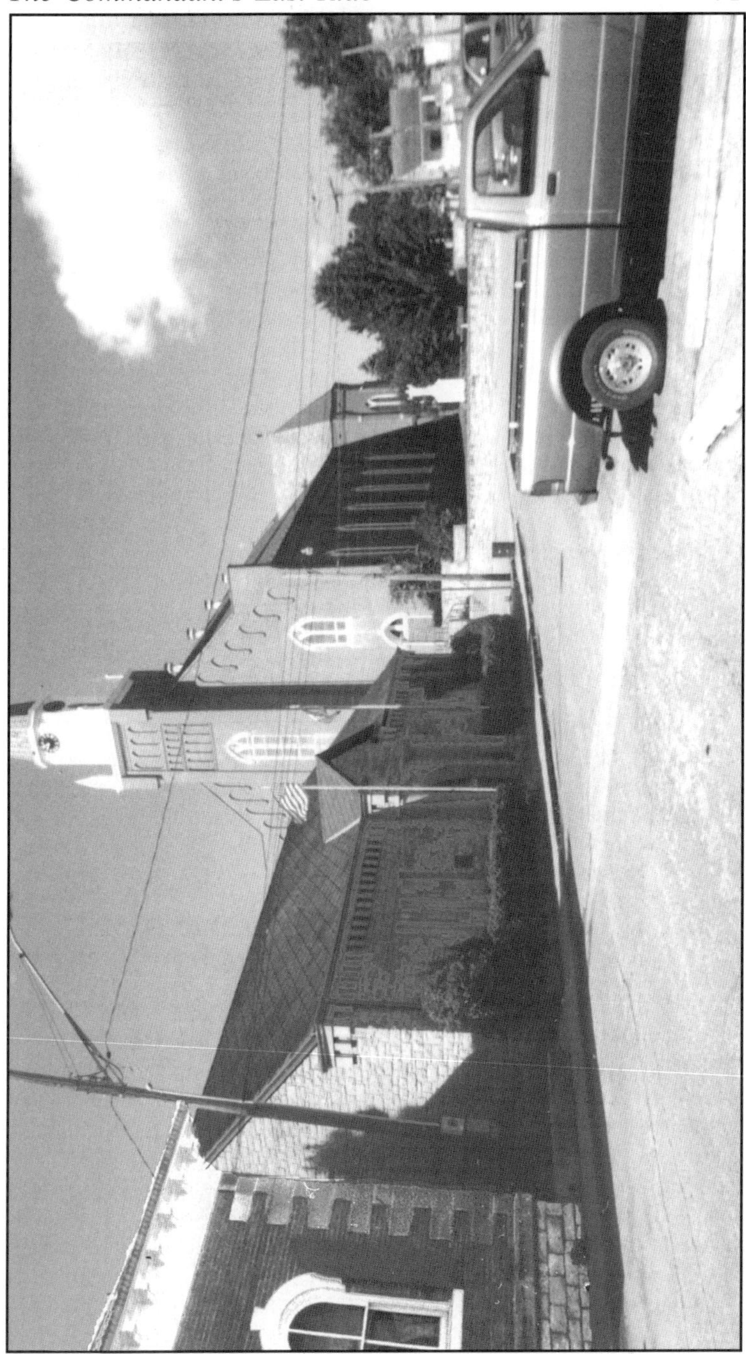

By the 1830s, the log church was in poor condition. Under the guidance of Father Dahmen, a Vincentian, a new rock church was constructed. It was consecrated November 12, 1837, with Bishop Rosati present. The attractive stone church served a generation of Ste. Genevieve patrons. It gradually proved to be too small, as Ste. Genevieve continued to grow in the nineteenth century.

By the 1870s, a move was underway to expand it or to build a new church. The only other option was splitting the parish in half. Work began on the current brick edifice in March, 1876. The cross was placed on the steeple November 1, 1879 the dedication was held September 29, 1880, with the Right Reverend P.J. Ryan, coadjutor bishop of St. Louis, performing the ceremony.

Built in a Gothic Revival style. It was designed by Father Francis Xavier Weiss, the pastor for many years. Odile Valle, widow of Felix Valle, gave $18,000 – three-quarters of the cost – toward the construction. It was built on the foundation of the stone church. The foundations are still visible in the cellar. They were left to provide additional support for the colonnade that separates the nave from the aisles.

The church was again enlarged under the leadership of Father Charles L. Van Tourenhout in 1911. Needing more seating capacity, "Father Van" had the rear wall removed and erected a hexagonal apse and two small transepts. New alters were added at that time. Much of the original brick work survives, including brick pilasters framing the aisle windows.

The church is linked by a covered passageway and garage to the 1925 rectory, an American Foursquare with a Spanish Colonial style stone entrance way. The parish welcomes visitors to step inside and admire the well-maintained Gothic interior, any time services are not being held.

Commandant François Vallé II, his wife, Marie Carpenter Vallè, Francois Corset, the *chantre*, and pastors James Maxwell and Henri Pratte are all buried below the church nave.

Old Valle School **61 DuBourg Pl.**

This double pile limestone building was built by Father Francis Xavier Weiss, shortly after he became pastor in 1865. He hoped to establish a Christian Brothers college here, but was unable to secure the services of the teaching brothers. Instead he moved in himself, using the attractive building as the rectory.

Known as "Old Valle" today, the two-story structure has symmetrical fenestration and round arched window and door openings. The exterior maintains much of its nineteenth century appearance, other than the original entrance – facing the square — being filled in. It became the first Valle High School in 1924. A stone addition was added to the South in 1937.

Old Jail/Old Courthouse

Some ten years before the current courthouse was built, Ste. Genevieve County added two major additions to the square. The twin jail and Old Courthouse were both built in the 1870s, in the ornate Italianate style. The jail was built after the previous "calaboose" burned.

Local oral tradition has long said that the 1821 log courthouse was merely remodeled into the Italianate courthouse of 1871. No real evidence has ever been offered, backing that theory. It would appear that both structures were built from scratch in the Italianate style. Both have survived years of use and disuse fairly well. The county has obtained grants to secure both buildings and to study restoration options.

The buildings offer many Victorian era decorative details on the facade, including limestone quoins, gabled pediments in the center of each side, wide, bracketed eves and the flat-topped roof with decorative iron castings. Exaggerated keystones in the arched window heads are another period touch.

65 / 21 S. Third

One of the most pristine surviving examples of a nineteenth century courthouse in Missouri, the Ste. Genevieve County Courthouse is the only true example of an Eastlake building in town. The original section was built in 1885, with additions in 1915 and 1987.

Built during the city's massive 150th anniversary celebration of the move from the old town site, the brick structure was designed by architect Jerome B. Legg. In the words of the HABS report, it "is a fine example of the decorative exuberance of the post-Civil War period." The springers and enlarged keystones of the arched window heads add important decorative elements, as does the colorful use of white stone in colorful contrast to the red brick. The bracketed balcony – also painted white – adds to the effect, along with the peaked roof and the projecting center bay of the south façade, itself. In a meticulous state of preservation, it adds much to downtown Ste. Genevieve.

The Old Jailhouse was built in the 1870s.

Southern Hotel

146 S. Third

The Southern Hotel, historically known as the John Donohue House, is an imposing and historic structure. The grand building traces its construction back to a cataclysmic event that literally rocked southeast Missouri.

The building was originally dated "circa 1820" by the HABS team of the 1980s. During the intervening years, though, owners Mike and Barb Hankins have conducted a thorough restoration and have had private dendrochronology tests done. The results moved the estimated construction date of the building back by several years. According to the tree ring findings – on file with the U.S. Department of Interior, wood used in the Southern Hotel dates to 1811 and 1813. This leads to the theory that the construction was well underway when the devastating New Madrid Earthquakes of December, 1811 and January, 1812 struck. Work seems to have halted until some time in 1813.

Archival research verifies this. John Donohue was also facing a legal challenge from neighbors Louis and Marie LaPorte at this time. The LaPortes filed suit against Donohue February 12, 1813 because he was constructing a large building which blocked the LaPortes' access to their property and had run them off his land at gun point. It mentions "a brick house which the said John has commenced building." Apparently the animosity between Donohue and his neighbors had coupled with earthquake damage to delay construction.

The building was originally a large residence for Donohue – a man with a serious gambling problem. Built with a central hall, like most true

Federal style buildings, it was a very sophisticated structure for the Upper Mississippi Valley of 1813. The Hankinses, though, are still convinced that one section of the building goes back to about 1800 and was constructed by Commandant François Vallé II – originally without a center hall.

Joe Vorst bought the building sometime before the Civil War and called it The Southern Hotel. Around1870 he added the dormers that line the roof today.

The cellar, with its thirty-two inch walls, kept the temperature fifty-five to fifty-six degrees year-round. Old-timers have recalled ice being kept in the cellar as late in the summer as August. The cellar included a "keeping room," which was the kitchen. There is evidence of a fireplace and half a beehive oven being there.

An original bedroom is directly above the keeping room and should have been warmer in the winter. Hankins believes the owner may have stayed there while the rest of the house was being completed and that a temporary roof may have covered it.

The building still has its twelve fireplaces – some of which are used to create a cozy mood for guests during the winter. The parlor, meanwhile contains a nice Federal period mantle with reeded pilasters.

The building was renovated in 1950 and reopened as an eleven-unit furnished apartment complex with fifty-six steam radiators and modern electricity. It operated until about 1980, then sat empty for several years. The Hankinses, who bought the old hotel in 1986, have restored it to its early splendor, including an inspiring garden in back of the building. The Southern is now a fine bed and breakfast establishment, known for its atmosphere, Victorian country antiques and fine cooking.

It has been featured in national magazines and on a national PBS television cooking program, *Country Inn Cooking With Gail Greco*. Its game room includes a handcrafted pool table, made for The Southern Hotel in St. Louis (supposedly named after this one) in 1875.

Did you know?

In March, 1897 Joseph Lalumondiere and Southern Hotel owner Joe Vorst placed a friendly wager on the heavyweight boxing championship match between "Gentleman Jim" Corbett and Robert Fitzsimmons.

When Fitzsimmons knocked out the champ in the 14th round, Lalumondiere had to push Vorst "around the primary streets" of Ste. Genevieve in a wheelbarrow., according to the March 27, 1897 *Ste. Genevieve Fair Play.*

John Price House/Old Brick

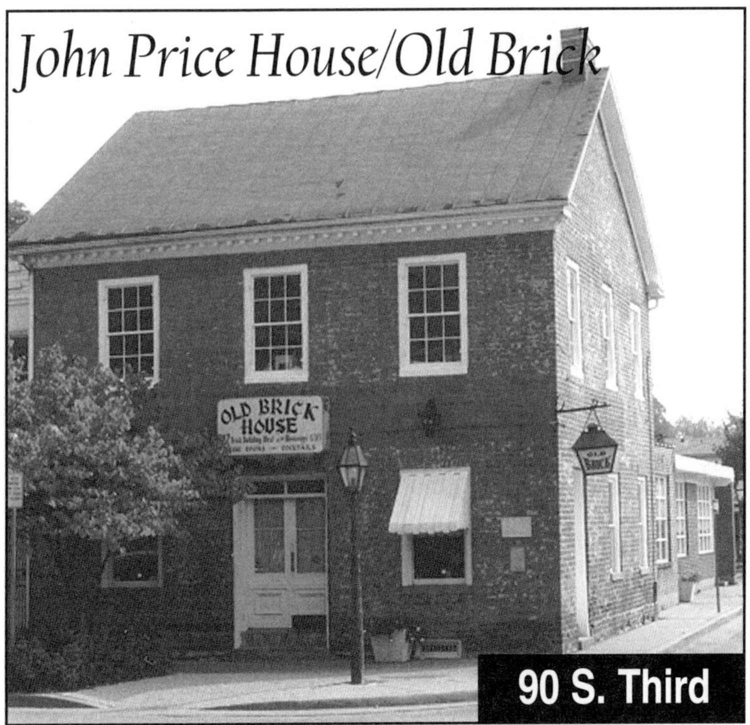

90 S. Third

Of enormous historic and architectural significance, the John Price House, now home of the Old Brick Restaurant, has long been said to be the oldest surviving brick building west of the Mississippi. While this has never been substantiated, neither has there ever been a line forming of challengers with older buildings.

Built about 1804 with hand-fired bricks – definitely fired within twenty miles of Ste. Genevieve, according to chemical analysis, and probably fired on the spot, the Federal double pile building preserves much of it original exterior appearance. This includes a classical frieze under the cornice, which is very similar to that of the Felix Vallé House.

The HABS report calls this "a sophisticated ornamental detail." The old building also has an early nineteenth century mantle upstairs. Its collar beams and rafters are vertical sawn, as are the second floor ceiling joists. Those are let into huge hand-hewn beams that run the width of the building.

The building held the first district court after American rule came to the Louisiana Territory and has been a commercial establishment most of its life. A decrepit moonshine still has been found in the basement, an interesting vestige of the Prohibition era. The Old Brick is today one of the town's popular restaurants and gathering spots.

Okenfuss/Huck Building

302 Market

One of the older commercial buildings in the courthouse square vicinity, this corner building was built about 1860. Officially the Florian Huck Building, but locally known as the Okenfuss Building, its parapet gables and second story fenestration show evidence of a pre-Civil War construction date. It "subtly contrasts" with the later nineteenth century buildings, in the words of the HABS report.

Victorian era additions on the first floor give it a more interesting appearance. The receded corner entrance and it cast iron column support "is noteworthy in its own right," according to the report, and does not seem to detract from the building's original lines.

Ferdinand Roy/ Herald office

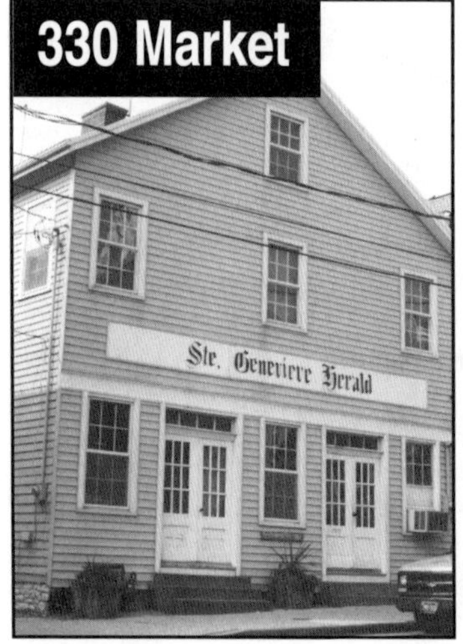

330 Market

The home of the weekly *Ste. Genevieve Herald* since the early twentieth century, this commercial vernacular building was built in 1865 by Ferdinand Roy. It was occupied for many years by pharmacist Charles F. Carssow. The huge old wooden case in the front room seems to date back to the Carssow era, including a shelf high on top, where laudanum, opium and other drugs may have been kept – out of reach.

According to the HABS reports, the gabled roof gives the building the look of a domestic structure rather than a commercial building. Also part of the *Herald* property is a Victorian era stairwell, leading to the second floor. This narrow brick addition (technically 342 Market Street) may be a fragment of an earlier building next door to the Roy building.

Thomure Ice House

Not visible from Market Street, this interesting little structure sits behind the *Herald* office, off of South Gabouri Street. (It actually attaches to Steve Marshall's cabinet shop, across from the Southern Hotel, at 181 South Third.)

A rare surviving example of a circa 1800 utility structure, it is believed to have been constructed as an ice house by J.B. Thomure. A tunnel is said to run from the ice house to below the Marshall building – where a livery stable once stood. According to Thomure family members, it was built in 1904 as a refuge for horses in case of fire.

It is believed the current parking lot was once at a higher elevation, allowing wagons to be loaded from the window. It appears that the roof was raised at some point, although no reason is known for the change today.

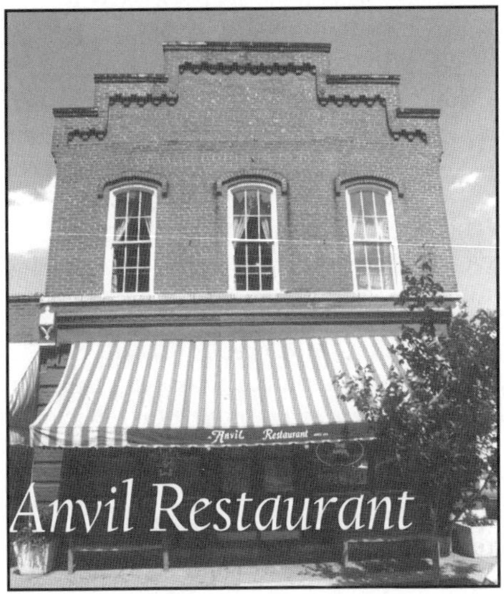

Anvil Restaurant

44 S. Third

Built between 1850 and 1870, this brick wall commercial vernacular building is one of the older ones on the square.

Home of one of Ste. Genevieve's several popular restaurants, its façade maintains much of its original appearance. Inside the brick walls add to the nineteenth century aura. The building has its original doors and Eastlake door jams.

Charles Gregoire House

51 S. Fourth

In most Missouri towns, this fine old Greek Revival home would be the most historic house in town. While the elegant side passage structure does not date to Ste. Genevieve's period of historic significance, it is still an important and attractive building.

Built about 1853, the Gregoire House is one of only two Greek revival side passes buildings in town. This urban style was much more common in cities like St. Louis. The Joseph Amoureux House (See page 13) is the other example. The brick building, bearing the name of Charles Gregoire who owned much of the block during colonial days, was obviously built with an eye for detail. The two and a half story façade has a horizontal band of limestone blocks which help define the half third story. Its three windows also help set it off from the lower floors, as the vertically aligned windows go from triple-hung on the first floor, to double-hung on the second, to tiny attic windows.

The rare side passage door is in a recessed entryway, under a strong cornice surround and featuring a frieze and engaged wooden columns. A "steamboat gothic" porch is on the rear, attached to an original one-story brick service wing. Much of the interior detail survives, including Doric mantelpieces and large sliding doors.

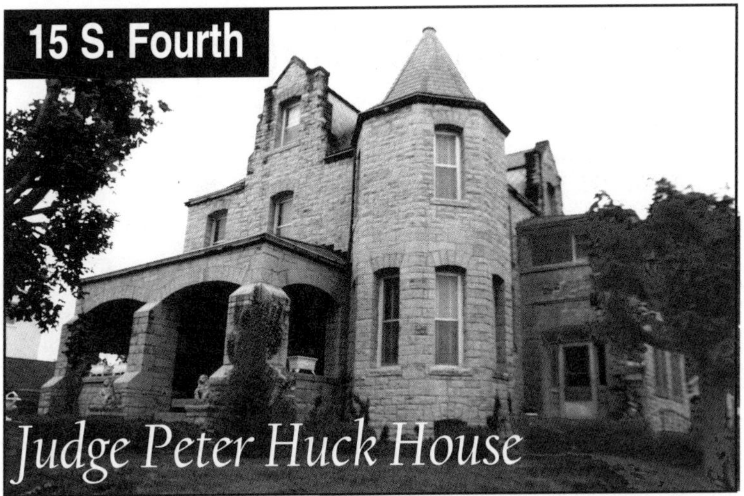

Although one of the village's early French Colonial homes had to go to make room for it, the Judge Huck House at 15 S. Fourth Street is a classic in its own right. Peter Huck, state legislator, circuit judge and prosecuting attorney, had the elaborate Queen Anne limestone home built in 1906, after razing the circa 1800 Charles Gregoire vertical log home.

The home represents one of the few limestone houses built in Ste. Genevieve in the twentieth century. It complements its early nineteenth century ashlar stone predecessors and lends a regal dignity to the downtown district. The HABS reports call it "the finest example of the late Queen Anne style in Ste. Genevieve."

It features an octagonal corner tower with a pointed hit roof and copper finial cap and a tall gable wall dormer facing Fourth street, with a stepped parapet. As the HABS report notes, the arched segmental porch bays "echo" the door and window lintels. The interior maintains most of its original woodwork and stained glass windows that may have come from Tiffany's.

Did you know?

The first known newspaper in Ste. Genevieve was the Correspondent & Ste. Genevieve Record, published 1821-1823. It was followed by the State Gazette, 1831-1833; the Southern Gazette, 1833; the Missouri Democrat, 1833-1850; The Pioneer, 1849-1850; The Creole, 1850-1851; and The Independent, 1852-1861. No issues are known to have survived of any of these publications.

Guibourd-Valle House

Whether or not his loyal slave Moros really slipped Jacques Guibourd out of Santo Domingo in a rum barrel during the island's slave uprising of 1792, as local tradition has it, Guibourd still casts a long and interesting shadow over Ste. Genevieve history.

Born in France, Guibourd spent much of his life on the French colonial sugar island (now Haiti) before fleeing to France during the slave revolt. There, he found his homeland torn by revolution and opted to head for America "sad, ill, and without resources," according to his son Omer' s diary – and eventually to Ste. Genevieve. Once here, he received a Spanish Land Grant in 1799 and married Ursule Barbeau, from a wealthy Prairie du Rocher family.

According to dendrochronology and many other pieces of evidence, Guibourd had this fine Creole home constructed in 1806-1807. The large and well-preserved French Creole house is built of vertical, hand-hewn white oak logs,

These are the only original surviving colonial casement windows in Ste. Genevieve.

mortised into a sill and infilled with *bouzillage*. It was modified somewhat during the nineteenth century, but still maintains much of its original fabric. Nearly all the visible structural members are hand-hewn.

One of the most amazing features of the Guibourd-Vallé is its awe inspiring Norman kingpost truss system. This is probably the most amazing of several noteworthy trusses in Ste. Genevieve and is more than worth the nominal admission fee, itself. A brick wing was added to the rear of the house at a much later date.

Jacque Guibourd died in 1812 – and Moros supposedly drowned during the 1844 flood, but the old home stayed in the Guibourd family until 1907. It continued to gradually deteriorate and was near the point of no return by 1931. It was then purchased by Jules Vallé, a direct descendant of Jean Baptist Vallé, and restored in the first of many local restoration projects.

This box lock — believed to be original — is one of many unusual examples of colonial hardware in Ste. Genevieve

Vallé and his wife, Anne Marie, both members of the St. Louis Social Register, decorated and filled the house with tasteful antiques and portraits of the Vallé ancestors. After Jules died in 1949, Anne Vallé traveled even more widely and filled the house with her exquisite antique collection. She died in December, 1971 and the house eventually found its way into the loving hands of The Foundation for Restoration of Ste. Genevieve, Inc. The Foundation has maintained the home ever since. It has operated as a tour house since 1973 – marking its twenty-fifth anniversary of being open to the public in 1998.

More than any other house in Ste. Genevieve, the Guibourd-Vallé has been the subject of numerous ghost stories and has been mentioned in more than one book on the subject of hauntings. Everything from Spanish soldiers to the ghosts of Mrs. Vallé's two dogs have been said to show up

Two guests check out the Guibourd-Valle attic during the 1998 open house, marking it being open to the public for twenty-five years.

at night. Some strange incidents, though, were explained a quarter of a century later, when two former teenage tour guides recalled "helping" the ghost stories along by making a first floor chandelier jingle at the right moment of the other guide's ghost spiel by stepping on a special spot in the attic floor.

Ghosts or no ghosts, the Guibourd-Vallé is one of the city's major historic sites and maintains Anne Vallé's outstanding antique collection. Her magnificent gardens are also preserved and are part of the house tour.

Leon Yealy House — 406 Jefferson

Expanded and turned into a bed and breakfast late in the twentieth century, this fine old Italianate brick home at the southwest corner of Fourth and Jefferson Streets is once again a private residence.

The two-story house, built about 1887, has a T-shaped plan like many Italianate buildings. The porch maintains well-preserved woodwork, characteristic of the style. Windows and bracketed eaves are also original and help maintain the nineteenth century look. The twentieth century addition – facing Fourth Street – only slightly hampers this appearance.

Father Francis Yealy, Ste. Genevieve historian and author,was born in this house.

Sometimes called the Simon Hubardeau House, this attractive ashlar stone home was actually built about 1817 by Jean Baptiste Hubardeau, Simon's son. Simon Hubardeau was one of the true characters of colonial Ste. Genevieve. Carl J. Ekberg has documented some interesting situations Hubardeau found himself in, due to an apparently juvenile nature.

The Hubardeau House is one of several fine examples of early nineteenth century ashlar limestone buildings in Ste. Genevieve. Built without a central hallway, the original stone section contained two large first floor rooms and an exterior doorway for each room. A brick wing was added to the back in the 1860s and most of the interior woodwork seems to have been replaced about that time. Greek Revival influences seem evident in the addition. Unbraced, vertical sawn rafters and hand-hewn cellar joists in the stone section seem to be original.

Its bright red shutters contrasting with the rich beige ashlar stone, the building is one of the city's more attractive structures. Well maintained, it is occasionally rented out as an elegant guest house.

Did you know?

Sam Ankersheill may have run the first service station in Ste. Genevieve. An August 24, 1912 ad proclaimed "Automobiles overhauled, repaired, bought, sold and traded by Sam Ankerscheill.

His shop was located on Main Street and included a "trouble car," or tow truck.

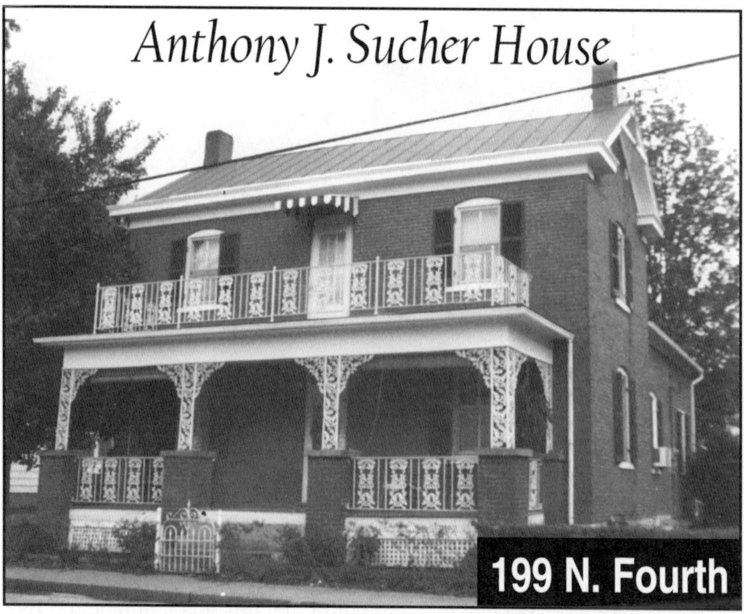

In a town where austere colonial buildings and grand nineteenth century structures compete for attention, a simple, yet elegant house like this one can go overlooked. Anchoring its corner at Fourth and Washington Streets, though, its simple charm is noticed by many.

A brick I-house, dating to about 1880, it was built with some Italianate features, such as projecting eaves, an arch above the fanlight and shallow-arched windows. Its wrought iron porch supports and second floor porch railing add to the elegant effect, as do the stone pilasters on the porch.

Did you know?

Flash flooding of the North and South Gabouri Creek has often proven to be more of a danger to Ste. Genevieve than river flooding. Ravaging flash floods hit Easter weekend, thirty-five years apart, seriously impacting the Third Street part of town.

In 1922 a house was washed off its foundation and against the third street bridge, 300 yards away. In 1950 fifty families were "literally swept from their homes" at 1 a.m., Easter morning, according to the *Ste. Genevieve Fair Play.*

Thursday, August 2, 1849

Thursday morning also dawned unseasonably cool and the com mandant again felt up to seeing the town. Only light showers had hit the previous evening and the streets were still in decent shape.

"The river's starting to rise, Commandant," Leandre said, as Vallé eased down his front steps.

"We don't have to worry," the commandant said with a toss of the head. "It was too dry this summer."

"I don't want to see another flood like the last one," the young man said.

"Oh, 1844?" Valle asked, stopping at the gate. "Yes, I was amazed. I don't know which was worse. It or *L'anne des grandes eaux* – 'Year of the Great Waters,' which was 1785."

"I've heard it mentioned many times," Leandre said.

"It covered the old village to the chimneys," the old man continued, staring to the East. "We had to camp out in the hills that summer and live like Indians."

"Did everyone move to the new town after that?" Leandre asked.

"Not right away, no," he replied. "A few were already living up here. We had so much invested down there. We tried to hold on for several more years. We really thought we were out of the river's reach up here."

He looked around muddy South Main.

"But it found us in forty-four, didn't it, Leandre?"

"It found us, Commandant."

And the cholera found us in forty-three, he thought with a shiver.

Sampson drove the commandant to Memorial Cemetery first. There he tramped among the graves of his old cohorts and friends. Louis Bolduc, Jean Baptiste Pratte, Jean Baptiste and Vital St. Gemme Beauvais. And, of course, Jeanne. The old man squatted down by the tombstone that would eventually have his own name chiseled above his wife's.

It probably won't be long, my dearest, he thought, gingerly laying a hand on the stone. Jeanne Barbeau.'s father had constructed Fort de Chartes. They had lived in Prairie du Rocher, just across the river. How well he remembered their first meeting, when he was in town, calling on Monsieur Barbeau in behalf of the ailing Papa Vallé. She had answered the door. A year later they were married. He smiled sadly before painfully rising to his feet. *Soon. Soon.*

The commandant was pleased a few minutes later to see Firmin Rozier

The commandant didn't try to hide his liking for the Rozier boys.

overseeing a pair of slaves at work in the yard of the Old Louisiana Academy – now being called Ste. Genevieve Academy. The young man put down the shovel he was leaning on and hurried over to the carriage.

"So you're still determined to reopen a school, are you?" Vallé greeted him.

"Yes sir," Rozier recalled, wiping sweat from his brow. "There is a tremendous amount of work to be done, but it's still a fine building. I may wind up having to add another wing to it, though."

"I hope you have fewer headaches than we had with it," the commandant said. "I was one of the original directors when the Academy opened, you know. We had no trouble recruiting students. Getting the parents to pay their bills was another matter!"

Rozier pardoned himself for a moment and gave instructions to one of the slaves who had just finished resodding a portion of the lawn.

"By the way, young man," the commandant quipped when he returned, trying to sound stern. "Just what are your intentions with my granddaughter?"

Firmin had been courting his granddaughter, Julie Vallé, for some time.

"Oh, most honorable, I assure you!" Firmin said, holding up his hands with a grin.

The two shared a laugh.

"Your father tells me you're considering running for the legislature," Vallé said in a moment.

"I'm thinking, yes sir," Firmin answered. "I'm a little bit torn, to be honest. Things are starting to really go well here, with the law office and the academy. But …"

"But you feel the calling."

"Yes sir, I suppose I do."

In a moment a rider on horseback pulled up beside the carriage. Firmin's younger brother Charles carefully climbed off the horse, which Firmin held by the reigns. The younger man eased himself down and, using two walking canes, hobbled toward the buggy.

"Colonel Vallé!" he exclaimed. "It's so good to see you out."

"Charles," he replied with a smile. The commandant didn't try to hide his liking for the Rozier boys – especially young Charles who had never let a crippling leg condition hinder him. "They tell me you've succeeded in straightening out Firmin's law practice."

Charles laughed a good-natured laugh. He had graduated just that spring from St. Vincent's College in Cape Girardeau and had joined Firmin at his law office.

"It didn't need much straightening," he said. "Firmin, or 'General Rozier,' as everyone's calling him now, already had a good little practice going."

"So how do you find the study of law?" Vallé asked Charles. He knew many young men – like Augustine Menard's husband Louis – who had considerable talent in the field, but had opted to pursue other interests.

"I love it," he said with a smile. "Although …"

Vallé looked at him expectantly, as he looked down at his crutches with an embarrassed smile.

"Oh Lord, here we go again," Firmin moaned.

"I've also been thinking about a newspaper," Charles said, looking back at the old man. "As much as I enjoy law, I really feel this urge, this desire to see my thoughts in print and to help inform the community."

"I'll declare!" Vallé quipped. "I never would have believed it. Two of Jean Ferdinand's sons who hate money! One wants to teach school instead of study law and the other wants to run a local newspaper!"

All three laughed.

"I fear that's about the way Father *does* see it," Firmin said, shaking his head.

"Well, if a man isn't enjoying his work, then his work probably won't amount to much anyway," the old man said. "Personally I've loved what I've done."

"You mean, 'getting rich'?" Firmin cracked. All three shared a hearty laugh before the triumvirate broke up to pursue their daily tasks.

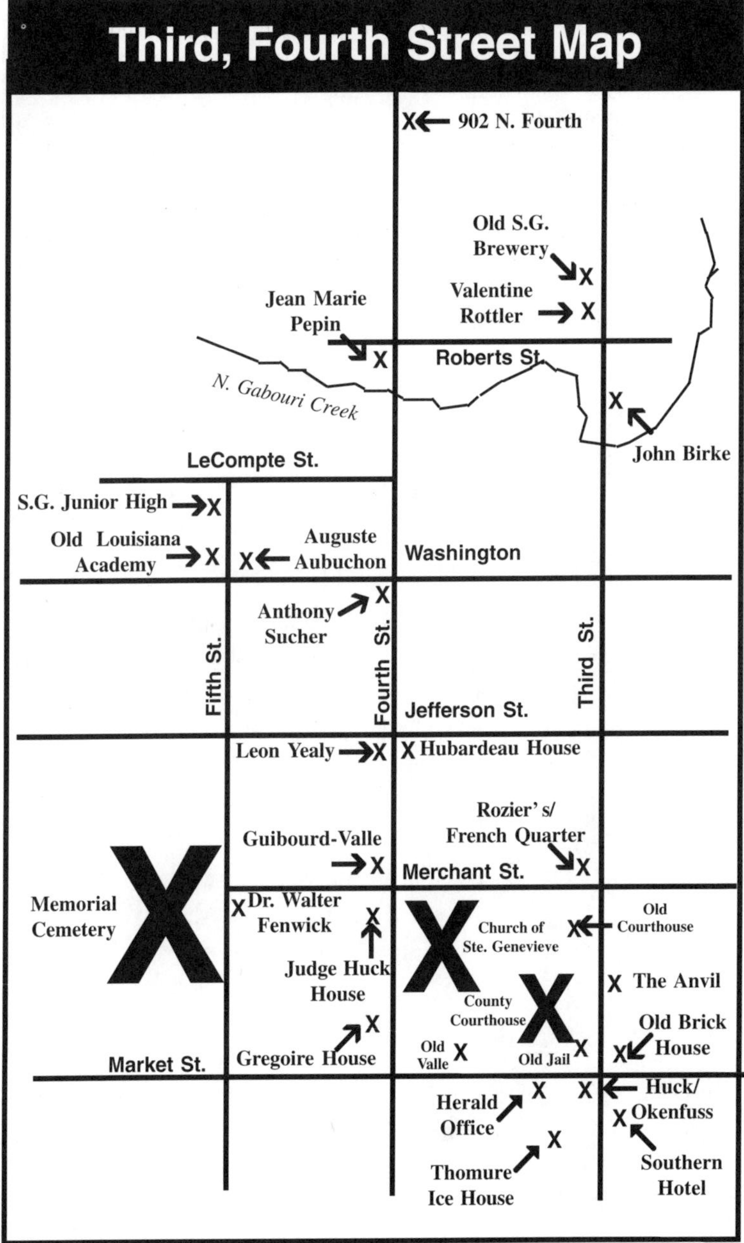
Third, Fourth Street Map
902 N. Fourth
Old S.G. Brewery
Valentine Rottler
Jean Marie Pepin
Roberts St.
N. Gabouri Creek
John Birke
LeCompte St.
S.G. Junior High
Old Louisiana Academy
Auguste Aubuchon
Washington
Anthony Sucher
Fifth St.
Fourth St.
Third St.
Jefferson St.
Leon Yealy
Hubardeau House
Rozier's/ French Quarter
Guibourd-Valle
Merchant St.
Memorial Cemetery
Dr. Walter Fenwick
Judge Huck House
Church of Ste. Genevieve
Old Courthouse
The Anvil
County Courthouse
Old Brick House
Gregoire House
Old Valle
Old Jail
Market St.
Herald Office
Huck/ Okenfuss
Thomure Ice House
Southern Hotel

The construction of the Old Louisiana Academy in 1808 signified more than a change in architectural styles in Ste. Genevieve. It also helped signal the town's emergence as a small but certainly not insignificant community in its new nation.

The first publicly funded school in the Louisiana Territory – and quite likely the first outside of the original thirteen colonies, the Academy smacked of the egalitarian vision of President Thomas Jefferson. Unfortunately, financial realities never really allowed the school to succeed.

Despite sitting empty nearly fifty of its first one hundred and eighty-five years and suffering damage from the New Madrid Earthquakes, vandalism and wildlife inhabitation, the grand old building has survived and has been painstakingly restored. In fact, it was saved from the ravages of time and neglect twice during its long life.

The Louisiana Academy was a bold undertaking in 1808. Children of leading families up and down the Mississippi River Valley were recruited for the school. Collecting the tuition owned them proved to be a frustrating enterprise for the directors, who included Jean Baptiste Vallé, Jean Baptiste Pratte and Father James Maxwell. Within a few years the academy folded. It was reopened by the renowned Christian Brothers, who opened a school in the limestone building. Evidence has recently emerged that the brothers had to deal with some damage from the 1811-1812 New Madrid Earthquakes. Some of the Academy's windows are still slightly off-line today. It was the teaching order' s first school in the Western Hemisphere and again, children from leading families from near and far attended. This venture, too, fell through, and the building was abandoned again in 1823. The original builder, Irishman William Shannon, wound up taking title to the delinquent property.

The building sat empty, gradually deteriorating until it came to be known as "the haunted house on the hill," clearly visible from riverboats of the day. (The river channel was closer then and few trees stood in town, due to the riverboats' incessant demand for fuel.) It was said to glow eerily in the moonlight.

General Firmin A. Rozier came to the building's rescue in 1849, restoring the fine old ashlar stone structure. He eventually added the fine brick wing on back and launched The Ste. Genevieve Academy in 1854. Once again the old hall was filled with enthusiastic young voices. The Civil War forced the closing of the school and the Academy wound up being Rozier' s personal residence.

The wealthy Rozier decorated the mansion in the Greek Revival style, turning it into what was called the grandest house in Ste. Genevieve. Rozier was a huge figure in Ste. Genevieve history, serving as a state representative and state senator, building a plank road to Farmington and fighting tirelessly for a railroad line to the old town. The General died in 1897 after leaving behind the first written history of Ste. Genevieve, *Rozier' s History of the Early Settlement of the Mis-*

sissippi.

The building – gradually deteriorating – remained in the Rozier family until 1935, when it was sold to the Ste. Genevieve School District for $8,500. A new high school was built next door and the dozens of slave cabins and other pieces of history were cleared away. The Academy was put to various uses, including housing for young teachers. It also sat empty much of the time.

When Tim Conley bought the Old Louisiana Academy in 1994 he found the1854 brick wing in sad shape. (avove) After some five years, Conley was able to enjoy the same shady balcony (below) on which the general had entertained guests a century earlier.

By the time current owner Timothy G. Conley bought the Academy in 1994, it was near the point of no return. Termites, bats and other life forms had made their home in the old building. He spent several years of his life returning the old home to the splendor of Rozier' s era. Conley has attempted to return the 1854 wing as closely as possible to the era in which the General was there and the limestone wing to the days of the original Louisiana Academy. He has tried to match the General's refined good tastes in colors and style and has restored many fine pieces of antique furniture and other items to add to the ambiance.

Some formal architectural plans seem to have been used, since the building was built with a central hallway and symmetrical window and door arrangements. Joists in the cellar are hand-hewn and Conley has uncovered the huge original kitchen fireplace there. A dumbwaiter was used during the Rozier era to transport food from the cellar.

Much of the surviving woodwork in the 1808 wing is original. Due to termite damage, Conley was forced to replace more of the original fabric than he would have preferred. All replication has been painstakingly done, with great care for authenticity. Today the Old Louisiana Academy is once again one of the finest homes in the region.

Auguste Aubuchon 467 Washington

Although it has deteriorated considerably during recent years, this circa 1800 French Creole cottage is still an excellent example of Ste. Genevieve's colonial architecture. Auguste Aubuchon received a grant for a farm lot in *le Grand Champ* in 1787 and probably received this house lot about the same time. The house was probably constructed by 1800.

The HABS reports notes that its dimensions and plans are similar to the Bequette-Ribault House, other than being a *poteaux sur solle* structure. Its original chimney of limestone is off-center, leading the HABS team to conclude that one of the original two rooms was larger than the other.

The western porch has been enclosed, but in the photo above, the original outline of the porch appears to be visible. The eastern porch – today considered the rear of the house – still maintains its Creole porch. Although the porch has badly deteriorated, it gives viewers an excellent glimpse of French colonial building practices.

Although its location next to the Old Louisiana Academy will never allow it to be truly appreciated as an historic educational and architectural structure in its own right, this 1936 WPA beauty is both. A huge debate was going on throughout 1935, as the city celebrated its (alleged) two hundredth anniversary. Several land sites for a new high school were reviewed, before the Academy Hill site was purchased from Tom Rozier for $8,500. This included the historic Academy building and grounds.

Although approval of funding was delayed by a squabble between New Dealers Harold Ickes and Harry Hopkins, it was finally approved in early October and work commenced. The ornate building opened for the 1936-37 school year, serving as Ste. Genevieve High school until the current high school was built in the mid 1960s. Since that time it has served as the junior high. It cost about $100,000, with the WPA paying $45,000 and the state chipping in $2,000.

Architects Bonsack and Pearce pulled out all the stops, including projecting bays with ornamented brick dormers, featuring circular windows and quoins. A cupola is perched atop the center

---

Did you know?

The** Ste. Genevieve Fair Play **was established in 1872, lasting more than 100 years. Many other local newspapers popped up over the years. The August 7, 1880** Fair Play **mentioned that four new papers — two in English and two in German — had been launched. "We have been starving to death for nine years and don't see how all of them are to make a living," a September 4 editorial remarked. The editor was right; none of the others survived. Its only real competitor, the** Ste. Genevieve Herald, **came along in May, 1882.

Dr. Walter Fenwick House

Although this small olive green house bears the name of Dr. Walter Fenwick, it appears to have been built a generation after his death.

Dr. Fenwick was a leading Ste. Genevieve citizen until he was killed in a pistol duel in 1811 – representative of the changing ways in Ste. Genevieve as the Americans continued streaming across the river.

Believed to have been built closer to 1850 by authors of the HABS report, the brick-nogged heavy-timber frame home presents an attractive face to both Merchant and Fifth Streets. The original part of the house has a hall and parlor design and some original pedimented door lintels and a few vertical sawn cellar joists remain.

According to the HABS report, "This interesting house may represent a class of small frame dwellings, only a few of which survive."

Memorial Cemetery

Fifth Street

This old burial ground is one of Ste. Genevieve's greatest prizes and greatest challenges. Now under the care of The Foundation for Restoration of Ste. Genevieve, Inc., the old Memorial Cemetery struggles against the elements and vandalism, yet remains a huge focal point for visitors and locals, alike.

As Gregory M. Franzwa put it in his time-honored *The Story of Old Ste. Genevieve,* "Here are buried the men and women who, two centuries ago, built the houses now bearing their names." The cemetery probably opened in the 1780s; the oldest legible grave is that of Louis LeClere, interred in 1796. Well known names such as Louis Bolduc, Jacques Guibourd, Jean Baptiste and Jeanne Vallé, Felix and Odile Vallé, Jean Ferdinand and Constance Rozier, Sen. Lewis F. Linn and Joseph Bogy are just a few.

Although many of the vaults are built in New Orleans style, this was purely decorative. The Ste. Genevieve founders are all buried six feet below. A local newspaper article in 1912 bemoaned the deteriorated con dition of the old burial grounds, closed in 1882. It has been a struggle to keep the historic markers and ground intact ever since. Local historian and preservationist Lucille Basler led the fight for many years. Uncertainty about the ownership of the cemetery was resolved in 1996, when the city accepted a transfer of any property right the Church of Ste. Genevieve might have held. Under this arrangement, The Foundation for Restoration, Inc., a non-profit organization, maintains the cemetery and has established a separate group, Friends of the Cemetery, which gratefully accepts donations toward the cemetery preservation.

Tax deductible donations may be sent to Friends of the Cemetery, care of The Foundation for Restoration of Ste. Genevieve; P.O. Box 88; Ste. Genevieve, MO 63670. Those donating $10 or more become members of the Friends of the Cemetery.

Jean Marie Pepin 699 N. Fourth

Although located off the beaten tourist path, the French Creole home of Jean Marie Pepin *dit* LaChance is one of the better-preserved French colonial homes in Ste. Genevieve. Built between 1815 and 1826, the vertical log structure has stone nogging between the logs and sill has original hand-hewn cellar joists. This led the HABS report to remark that "it was evidently better built than many extant houses of its size."

Much of the house's original – or at least very early – interior woodwork is still intact, including a beaded board paneling that encloses boxed stairs and two beaded board-and-batten doors on the interior of the house. The roof was apparently raised late in the nineteenth century and a frame addition was added to the rear.

A small smokehouse, dating back to the 1800s, stands behind the house.

Brick Queen Anne

902 N. Fourth

Another fine home that is rarely seen by visitors is this circa 1910 Queen Anne beauty. A two story brick house with the popular Queen Anne gable and hipped roof combination, it offers some intriguing exterior ornamentation.

A brick course at the eve line using light-colored bricks to represent quoins and decorative shingles in its gables, add to the pleasing aesthetics of the old home. Formed concrete foundation blocks, meanwhile, are designed to looked like rusticated ashlar stone.

Old Ste. Genevieve Brewery

Built by Valentine Rottler – probably in 1887 – this dilapidated but imposing structure is the only major example of a Richardsonian Romanesque building in Ste. Genevieve.

Rottler migrated from Baden, Germany at age twenty, in 1852, and settled in Ste. Genevieve County, at New Offenburg. There he became a partner in Satz & Company in 1855 and later became sole owner. That brewery burned in 1872. Bad luck continued to follow Rottler. He moved to Ste. Genevieve in 1872 and bought an existing brewery. In 1882 he bought this land and the neighboring lot and built the fine brick home next door. The next year he built a brewery which burned October 25, 1886.

Undaunted, Rottler "at once rebuilt and has now a fine substantial brick building, fully insured and having the latest and best machinery for the success of his business," according to the 1888 *Goodspeed's History of Southeast Missouri.*

Attempts to secure funding and/or tax credits for restoring the fine old structure have thus far proved difficult, since the Ste. Genevieve Historic District's period of significance is registered as running only into the 1840s. An attempt to restore the building as a micro-brewery met neighborhood opposition in the late 1990s, due to fear of an abandoned neighboring tavern reopening. The building, though aging, has all the exaggerated arches, impost blocks around window heads and other frills of the Romanesque style and would be a huge boon to the community if restored.

An older gable-roofed structure is attached to the brewery, hidden by a stuccoed brick façade. This could possibly be a surviving section of Rottler' s 1883 brewery.

Valentine Rottler House

501 N. Third

One of the most attractive German brick homes of the nineteenth century, this central hall I-house was built in 1882 by local beer baron Valentine Rotter. Rottler built the Old Ste. Genevieve Brewery next door, after a run of bad luck. Rottler, who migrated from Baden, Germany in 1852, was co-owner of a brewery in nearby New Offenburg. It burned in 1872 and Rottler moved to Ste. Genevieve and bought an existing brewery.

He bought this property in 1882 "on which he built his fine house, one of the finest in the city," according to *Goodspeed's History of Southeast Missouri.* The house is *still* a fine one, "especially handsome," in the words of the HABS report.

Its limestone lintels, sills and quoins stand out in marked contrast to the red brick. It maintains much of its original appearance, with sidelights, two-light window sash, and bracketed eaves all appearing to be original. The original interior floor plan still seems to be intact, as well. A brick summer kitchen is also on the lot.

Did you know?

Ste. Genevieve was known far and wide as a high school girls' volleyball power during the 1970s and 1980s, winning two state championships and finishing in the top four two other times. Nicknamed the Headhunters, they are believed to be Missouri's first high school girl's team to have its own nickname — totally independent of the boys' mascot.

John Birke Stone House

398 N. Third

One of the early stone houses in Ste. Genevieve, this fine home was built by blacksmith John Birke – probably between 1800 and 1812. The original stone building was one story, measuring approximately thirty-one by eighteen feet.

This house has been greatly altered, both inside and out. An upper half-story and rear addition were added early in the twentieth century and most of the interior was remodeled, as well. A few vertical sawn floor boards are still in the stone part of the house.

Perched alongside the North Gabouri Creek, the old home – like this part of town in general – has always been endangered by both Mississippi River floods and flash creek floods. The entire neighborhood is a collection of endangered historic gems, not always seen by visitors.

A few thoughts on privacy

For most readers of this book this note is not necessary. Lovers of historic homes and those able to appreciate an historic ambiance are generally thoughtful, polite people, whose visits are enjoyable for all.

Simply because this type of situation has occurred before, the author feels obliged to remind readers that the majority of buildings included in this work are private residences. Only a handful are tour houses, while a number are places of business. A few sit empty, awaiting an appropriate use. Any building that does not have an "open" or "entrance" sign should be considered private property.

This is only brought up because more than one restorer of an historic home in Ste. Genevieve has described episodes to the author in which they were upstairs, relaxing, only to find total strangers inside their house – apparently looking for a tour guide! Some of our historic home owners are pleased to invite strangers in who admire their homes; many are not.

No one enjoys having meals or rest interrupted by a visitor wanting to examine cellar joists. Of course Ste. Genevieve's historic home owners *do* take pride in their homes and generally enjoy discussing them. Common sense, naturally, should be the rule.

Many private homes are open for special tours from time to time. The Great River Road Interpretive Center (573-883-7097), Ste. Genevieve Convention and Visitors Bureau and the Ste. Genevieve Chamber of Commerce (573-883-3686, SGChamber@brick.net) can provide information on special house tour dates.

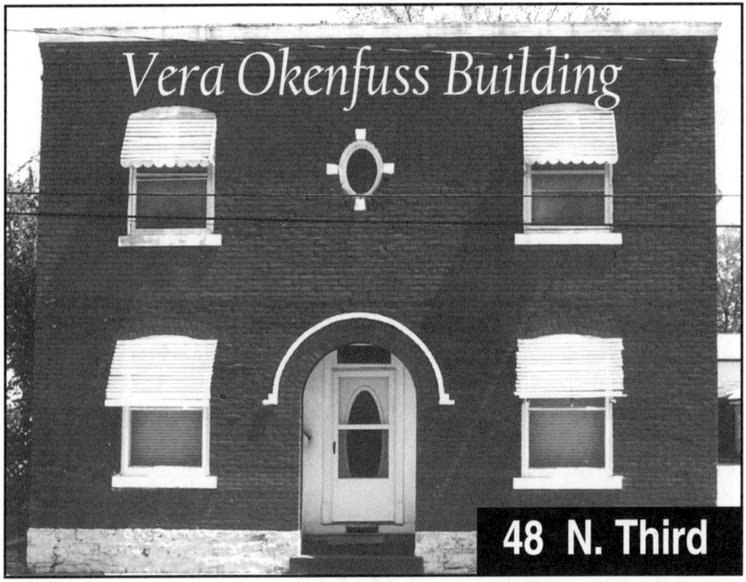

Only three examples of Richardsonian Romanesque or Romanesque Revival architecture survive in Ste. Genevieve. This small brick building is one, giving it a significant place among Ste. Genevieve's historic buildings. The arch above the doorway, with its attractive white border, is the only real evidence of the style. The small oval window with four white flagstone, set symmetrically above the arched doorway, adds to the charm of the building.

The HABS team determined in the 1980s that the building sits on the foundation of a circa 1810 structure which was apparently razed early in the twentieth century, when the current edifice was built. The hand hewn joists and foundations of original end chimneys are still visible in the basement. Late nineteenth century photos show a one-story brick building standing on this spot, with large end chimneys.

That afternoon more thundershowers hit Ste. Genevieve. The commandant relaxed on his deep *galerie* with a bottle of wine and a book. He dozed off briefly and dreamed of the childhood visit of the first Spanish officials to the formerly French community. Papa Vallé rolled out the red carpet for Don Francisco Ríu. The seven-year-old Jean Baptiste listened in wonder – and some bewilderment – as his father assured the Spanish official that the French Creoles in Ste. Genevieve were overjoyed to be Spanish subjects.

But the little English boy, Henry Marie Brackenridge, was also there and was only able to answer *"oui"* and *"non"* to several questions put forth by the Spaniard. The disturbing overlapping of time caused the commandant to awake with a start.

He chuckled at the thought of Brackenridge being in Ste. Genevieve during his own childhood. *I'll have to remember to tell Catherine about the dream at dinner,* he thought, struggling to his feet and heading back inside.

The rain had abated by the time the old commandant was washed and dressed for dinner. He couldn't help thinking of sons Louis and Jean Baptiste II, both of whom had died before middle age. He shared Odile's concern about Felix traveling to St. Louis during the cholera epidemic. Yet, as he had said, Felix was no one's fool and surely the Lord would watch over him. Tonight he would be dining with his other surviving son, François Baptiste and his wife of nearly forty years, Catherine St. Gemme Beauvais. He smiled at the thought of their wedding day. He would definitely have to share that Brackenridge dream.

To save the commandant from having to navigate the slippery steps and wade through the mud in his best outfit, powerful young Leandre picked him up and lowered him over the *galerie* railing to Sampson, who sat him in the buggy.

Sampson had to take it slower than usual, going up North Main, due to the huge mud puddles. That was fine with the commandant, who was able to check out that part of town. He shook his head at the massive new houses just being completed by two of his friend Rozier's other sons, Francis and Felix. Side by side, just north of Merchant Street, the handsome brick homes made an impressive addition to Main Street. Smaller brick buildings were also beginning to go up along North Main – mainly built by the ever-growing influx of German immigrants. *Nothing wrong with the Germans. You won't be able to call it a French town much longer, though.*

He waved to Eloy LeCompte, county treasurer and former sheriff, as they passed LeCompte's monumental stone home with an imposing two-story porch spanning the front. It was definitely one of the most impressive homes in town.

So was the cut stone beauty built by François Baptiste and Catherine. With ashlar stone on the front – facing the river – and field stone on the side, it was a real gem, itself. The commandant always enjoyed visiting it.

When Sampson pulled up in front of the house, one of Catherine's domestic slaves hurried out and instructed him to pull the carriage flush with the front door – even though it would leave horrendous ruts in the front yard. Sampson did so and the old man climbed out, right onto the front stoop.

"Odile was right!" François Baptiste exclaimed after the commandant had entered the main hall of the large home. "You *are* looking well!"

"I feel healthier than I have in some time," he said truthfully, leaning on his cane and examining the rearranged hall.

"And your slaves?" Catherine asked. Her husband immediately cast her a stern glance.

"My slaves?" the old man asked. "All fine, so far as I can tell. Why?"

"No reason, Father," François Baptiste said forcefully, offering him his arm and giving his wife another dirty look. "Come, sit down a while before dinner." Reluctantly, the commandant let the subject slide and accompanied his son into the parlor. He quickly pushed François Baptiste's strange behavior aside.

"I dreamt of Henri Brackenridge today, my dear," he said to Catherine, after they had all been seated. He quickly related the strange dream.

"Dear Henri," she said with a faint smile. "We heard from him at Christmas. He continues to do well in Pittsburgh."

"He would have done well anywhere," François Baptiste added, lighting a cigar.

"Very true," the commandant said, lighting one himself. "He was bright and curious."

"And very sweet," Catherine added.

"You've always been sweet on him!" her husband teased.

"I'll never forget your wedding day," the commandant said, gazing into his glass of brandy. "The way she carried on, I thought Madame Beauvais was being strangled by John Smith T. or some other culprit when she opened the front door!"

The other two roared with laughter.

"But it was the little English boy – all grown up!" he continued. "Such a coincidence that he happened to visit town the day of your wedding."

"And he hid out all day to avoid seeing any of us," Catherine mused, "just to avoid spoiling the surprise. He was so thoughtful."

"I wish all the Americans were!" her husband quipped.

They were still laughing when Annie announced that dinner was ready. Enjoying the best appetite he had in weeks, the commandant had a second helping and enjoyed another brandy and cigar afterwards. He and his son were enjoying the cool of the evening in front of the grand house when they were disturbed by a wail from beyond the house.

The commandant's aging but clear mind quickly put the pieces together.

"Why was Catherine inquiring about my slaves?" he asked. "Are yours ill?"

His son looked grimly at his boots, apparently not wanting to ruin the old gentleman's evening.

"The cholera?" the commandant asked.

François Baptiste looked up, surprised but relieved. He nodded his head.

I have a bad feeling about this, the old man thought. Instead he quietly crushed the remains of his cigar.

"Take care of yourself and your family," he said softly. "It appears that is has returned."

"It appears so," his son reluctantly agreed.

And I believe it will take me, the commandant almost added aloud.

"You take care, too, Father," François Baptiste said, embracing his father as the carriage pulled up.

They exchanged a long gaze. *He knows it, too*. The old commandant smiled.

"Till we meet again," he said with a tip of his ancient three-corner hat and climbed back into the carriage.

He asked Sampson to take him up to Little Rock Landing before heading home. *I doubt if I get to see the river again.* He first glanced up the hill, where lights emanated from the former home of his late son Jean Baptiste II. Like the lots where Felix and François Baptiste lived, the old man had given him a special deal on the land. He shrugged at the thought. *Old Rozier has done what he could to help his sons, too. And Papa did all he could for us. He* turned from the house, and gazed at the river, as Sampson pulled to a stop beside it.

It was high in its channel, despite the dry summer. Still, he knew it wasn't going anywhere this late in the year. Ste. Genevieve was safe from that threat. But the other … He shivered as he thought of the last cholera outbreak.

"Let's go!" he barked, hating to expose himself and Sampson to any germs that might be in closer proximity to the river or to the north of town. He knew the disease seemed to hit slaves first, as well as the very young – and the very old.

He smiled at the river as Sampson pulled away. Gazing over the river as the moon popped out between billowing clouds was one of the earliest childhood memories he could call upon. Now the same moon emerged from between clouds and cast a similar pattern on the rippling water. With a sense of contentment, the old commandant leaned back in the carriage and enjoyed the ride home.

Gazing over the river as the moon popped out between billowing clouds was one of the earliest childhood memories he could call upon.

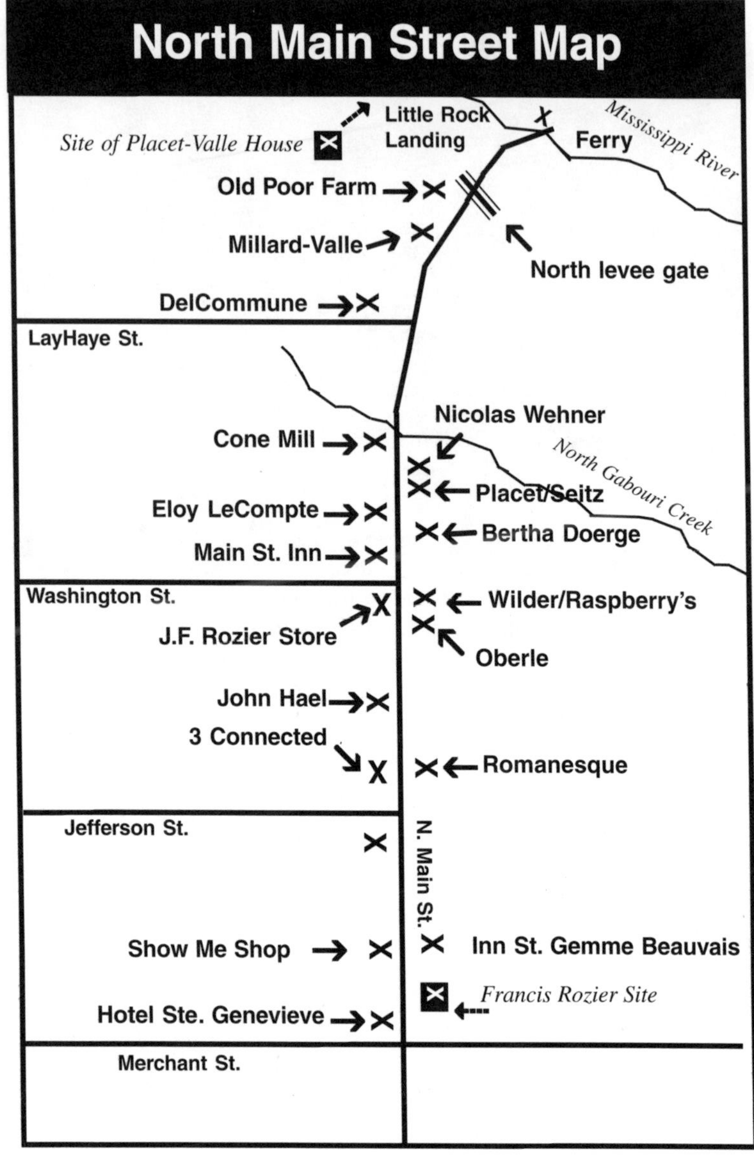
North Main Street Map
Little Rock Landing
Site of Placet-Valle House
Ferry
Mississippi River
Old Poor Farm
Millard-Valle
North levee gate
DelCommune
LayHaye St.
Nicolas Wehner
Cone Mill
North Gabouri Creek
Placet/Seitz
Eloy LeCompte
Bertha Doerge
Main St. Inn
Washington St.
Wilder/Raspberry's
J.F. Rozier Store
Oberle
John Hael
3 Connected
Romanesque
Jefferson St.
N. Main St.
Show Me Shop
Inn St. Gemme Beauvais
Francis Rozier Site
Hotel Ste. Genevieve
Merchant St.

Inn St. Gemme Beauvais

78 N. Main

The second generation of the Rozier family in Ste. Genevieve may have been the most successful of the accomplished clan. While patriarch Jean Ferdinand Rozier launched the family in the New World, the one-time partner of John James Audubon saw his children go on to establish a standard of living unimaginable when the elder Rozier came to Ste. Genevieve in 1811.

One sign of this success were the houses they built. In 1848-1849 two of the Rozier siblings, both highly successful businessmen, constructed fine brick mansions on adjoining plots on North Main Street. Felix Rozier's home has survived, while the Francis Rozier House was razed in 1957. Now housing the Inn Ste. Gemme Beauvais, a leading bed and breakfast establishment, the Felix Rozier House is believed to have been built in a Greek Revival style, with a side passage door. Two other example of these townhouses exist in town (the Joseph Amoureux at 102 S. Main and the Gregoire House at 51 S. Fourth).

University of Missouri architectural historians believe the northern half of the house was added later in the nineteenth century. The southern half of the façade, they note, is of Flemish bond, where the northern half is a common bond. The porch and the swan's neck pediment around the front door are twentieth century additions.

The home was bought by Lawrence Donze in 1923 and willed to Norbert Donze in 1948. It was among the earliest of several historic buildings he and his wife Frankye restored. It has operated as a bed and breakfast establishment ever since — supposedly the first in Missouri.

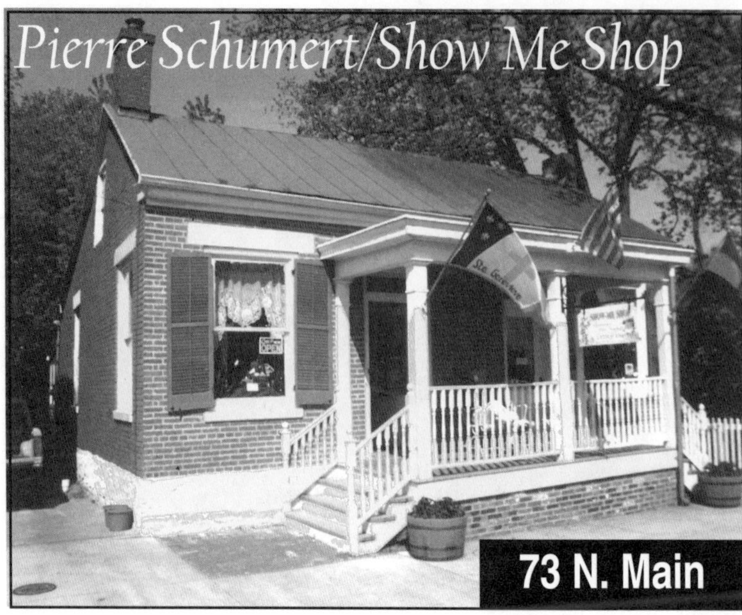

One of the best examples of the impact the wave of German migration had on local architecture in the mid nineteenth century, the current-day Show Me Shop is a testimony to the craftsmanship of the German vernacular house. Although it contains some definite Greek Revival influences – transoms over the doorways and flat limestone window lintels, the German brick vernacular style is dominant.

The basement under the original section of the house was apparently used as a kitchen. A fireplace opening can still be seen and a stairway leads to the first floor. Vertical sawn cellar joists can be seen in the cellar, as well. The original section of the house also contains some original finish work, which the HABS report indicates "appears to have been handcrafted rather than mass produced, including the transom sash and glazed, exterior cellar door."

The Pierre Schumert House, built about 1850, was one of the first German vernacular structures in town and lead off the North Main neighborhood of German vernacular, commercial vernacular and other nineteenth century buildings.

Did you know?

During the 1844 flood, Francis Rozier was said to have dove head-first off of a retaining wall ,into the flood waters at the corner of Main and Merchant.

Dr. Charles Hertich House

One of many historic homes in Ste. Genevieve that seems to be built on the foundation and basement of an older home, this Second Empire beauty dates to about 1850, with its current design elements added about 1880. The basement shows definite signs of dating back as far as 1810 or so.

Dr. Charles S. Hertich, a leading local physician, bought the house – apparently built by Amos Leavenworth between 1848 and 1850 – for $1,800 in 1850. At that time, Hertich was living in Long Prairie, MN, where President Millard Fillmore had appointed him as United States Surgeon to the Winnebego Indians. In 1851 he joined his wife, Mary Rozier Hertich, in Ste. Genevieve, where they resided in the home the rest of their lives.

The northern part of the house was built first. Dr. Osmund Overby, who led the HABS program of the 1980s, believes the original 1850 structure had two stories with a gable facing Main Street.

The mansard roof was added when Dr. Hertich remodeled and added onto the house in 1880, adopting the Second Empire look – one of Ste. Genevieve's few surviving examples of this popular late nineteenth century style. After sitting empty for several years, it is now a bed and breakfast, owned by Mark and Connie Smith, owners of the Inn St. Gemme Beauvais.

Connected commercial buildings

Connected today by the same tin roof, the Anton Klemmer House (101 N. Main), the Rozier-Hertich Building (109 N. Main) and the Peter Grassmuck House (117 N. Main) are good examples of the sturdy brick construction used by both German and American builders in Ste. Genevieve from about 1850, on.

The Americans seemed to have only rarely built with brick before the influx of German migration after the revolutions of 1848.

Interestingly, the Klemmer House (to the South) appears to be the oldest, with the Grassmuck House (farthest North) built second and the Rozier-Hertich Building built between the other two at a later date.

The Klemmer House, an Anglo-American vernacular I-house, seems to date to about 1850, with its six-light window sash, transoms and flat-arched window heads. The building – now office to a local attorney – seems to maintain much of its original façade.

The Rozier-Hertich building, built about 1880, may have originally been either a gable-roofed I-house or a commercial structure. The first floor window openings, though, may be original, which would suggest original use as a commercial building.

The Grassmuck House, also an I-house, probably did not have its Colonial Revival porch and balusters when built.

101, 109, 117 N. Main

The nineteenth century Klemmer, Rozier-Hertich and Grassmuck Buildings share a common roof.

122 N. Main

Romanesque building

Built around 1900, this building has been classified as commercial vernacular. Still, its rounded first floor doorway arch shows strong Romanesque influences.

Only two full-fledged Richardsonian Romanesque buildings survive in Ste. Genevieve. (The Ste. Genevieve Brewery at 555 N. Third and the Vera Okenfuss House at 48 N. Third.) While this structure cannot be classified as such, it certainly shows that the commercial structures at the turn of the last century were not devoid of popular stylistic influences.

The façade does not seem to have been altered much from its original appearance.

John Hael House

159 N. Main

Like the Pierre Schumert House at 73 N. Main, this circa 1860 German brick vernacular house shows some Greek Revival influences. It is also similar to the Firmin A. Rozier Store (124 Merchant). It's flat-arched stone window lintels and door and the transom above the doors all give hints of the Greek Revival influence. A later rear addition with arched window heads was added, along with bracketed eaves.

The façade still looks largely like it did in the nineteenth century and makes an important contribution to the historic North Main neighborhood. It is now rented as a bed and breakfast suite.

Did you know?

Ste. Genevieve resident Steve Bieser played for the New York Mets and Pittsburgh Pirates in 1997 and 1998 respectively.

Joseph Oberle House

Actually two connected buildings built a quarter of a century apart, the attractive red brick Oberle buildings mark the birthplace of the famed "Oberle Dog" sausage. The German vernacular brick structure to the North was built by family patriarch Joseph Oberle some time after 1865, with the store building added to the south about 1890.

The HABS report glowed with praise for the "verticality of the façade" and the aesthetic merits of the structures. The older building "presents one of the most handsomely preserved nineteenth century facades on N. Main Street," according to the survey, its three-bay gable end "articulated in a restrained but sophisticated fashion." Its broad eaves with pronounced returns add to the façade's appearance, as well as the small fan-shaped window in the center of the gable.

The commercial structure to the right still maintains its original cast iron ornaments and screen door. A brick smokehouse still stands behind the buildings, bearing continued witness to the Oberle sausage legacy.

Francis Rozier Building

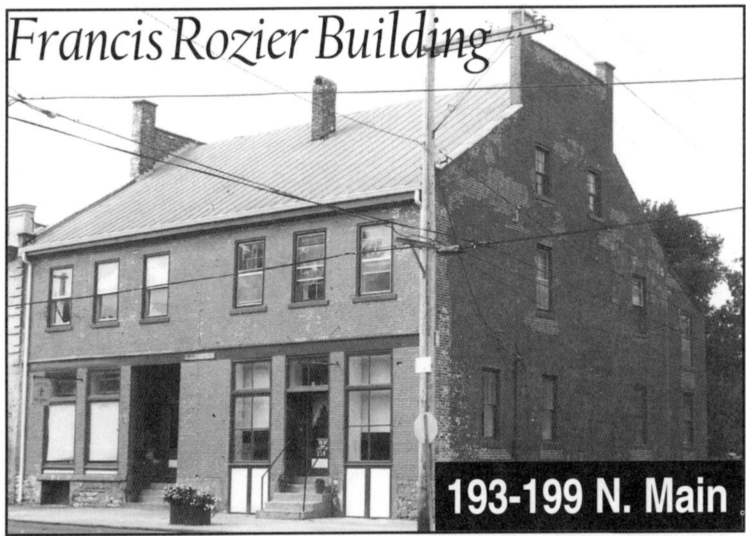

193-199 N. Main

While the current brick structure does not likely date back to 1836, when family patriarch Jean Ferdinand Rozier opened a store on this lot, it definitely goes back to his son Francis Rozier's mercantile business, prior to the Civil War. Probably built in the 1850s, this is actually two buildings, formerly connected by an interior doorway.

Anchoring the southwest corner of North Main and Washington, the imposing brick buildings still have their original parapet gables and six-light window sashes on the upper floors. Original structural cast iron columns are still visible in the first floor of the northern half of the building, which now hosts Ivy & Twigs, a plant and antique shop.

Henry Wilder/ Raspberry's

198 N. Main

This attractively restored commercial frame building dates back to about 1870. Built by Henry Wilder, it housed a popular tavern in the late nineteenth and early twentieth century.

The two-story building has a gable facing the street and has one shop window and several board-and-batten shutters that appear to be original. A huge bake oven is located in the cellar, under the one-story addition on the rear. It now hosts Raspberry's, an antique shop.

Meyer Hotel/Main Street Inn

One of the few Second Empire buildings in town, the former Meyer Hotel was built in 1882 by the widow Mary Meyer. (See "A Tale of Two Buildings.") Now operated as a fine bed and breakfast, the building has a square two-story plan with an attached ell and smokehouse.

The building has a mansard roof and bracketed eaves, characteristic of Second Empire style. At one time the Eloy LeCompte House next door was used for additional guest rooms for the Meyer Hotel. Main Street Inn has been featured in many national magazines since its restoration.

North Main Street offers an interesting mix of building styles.

Bertha Doerge House

Another one of the rare Second Empire Houses, this circa 1880 house was the home of Bertha Doerge (1836-1926), a leading Ste. Genevieve midwife. She was alleged to have birthed more babies than any local doctor ever did. Born in Berlin, Bertha Straube migrated to the U.S. in 1846. She graduated from the St. Louis School of Midwifing in 1876 and moved to Ste. Genevieve in 1878, where she married Captain Charles Doerge. She was said to have birthed more than 1,000 babies. The last one was her own great-great granddaughter.

"The building presents a fine example of domestic architecture in a style that reflects the post-Civil War taste for heavy, plastic ornament," the HABS report noted.

The second story dormers and the built-on second story face wall give it the mansard roof look of other Second Empire buildings, including the former Meyer Hotel across the street.

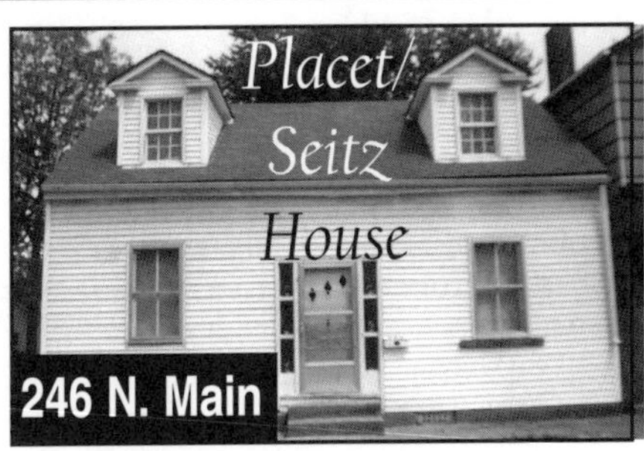

Controversy has surrounded the innocent looking white house at 246 N. Main. In 1865 or 1866, German émigré Valentine Seitz (1842-1930) either built this German vernacular brick-nogged, heavy-timber frame house from scratch or built it around a circa 1790 vertical log cabin, said to have been built there by Michael Placet. The house is still owned by descendents of Seitz, who insist they have seen the vertical logs during post-flood repairs to the house. Seitz was badly burned in the July, 1880 Cone Mill explosion (See "A Tale of Two Houses.") and carried back to this house to die. He pulled through, however, later became mill manager, and lived until 1930.

Misidentified as the Nicolas Wehner House (which is next door) in the HABS survey, the house features some Greek Revival ornamentation, including a large beaded board return and sidelights and a transom around the entry door. Pedimented door and window heads are on the interior.

Eloy LeCompte House

231 N. Main

Built about 1832, this Anglo-American vernacular I-house was made of sturdy limestone. Originally it had an attractive two-story porch which extended across the entire façade. An 1892 newspaper article claims that passengers disembarked from a river-going vessel which docked at the front porch during the disastrous 1844 flood.

This was probably the finest house in town for a number of years after its construction. It was one of the later of several important limestone buildings built during the first half to the century. After Anglo-American influences began inundating the old French village early in the 1800s, the use of brick and limestone from the huge river bluffs became very popular. The Old Louisiana Academy, the Felix Valle State Historic Site, the Dufour Stone Building and the Simon Hubardeau House are others of the same general style.

The LeCompte House was damaged by a fire sometime in the twentieth century and its roof line had to be changed. (The old roof line is still visible on the limestone.) The deteriorating wooden porch was removed in 1940 and the ponderous front stoop was added.

It did not originally have a central hallway Most of the surviving interior woodwork date from a late nineteenth century remodeling. A beaded chair rail on the second floor and the hand-planed six-panel doors there are probably original, though.

It is rented as apartments.

A later German immigrant and leading Ste. Genevieve businessman of the late nineteenth century, Nicolas Wehner (1825-1897) moved to Ste. Genevieve in 1860 and opened a grocery store. He apparently built this large double entrance frame I-house sometime thereafter.

He established a lumber yard just across the North Gabouri Creek. The final vestiges of the old lumber yard were destroyed by the 1973 flood. "An enterprising man of undaunted courage and perseverance," according to his obituary, he "reclaimed almost entirely from the North Gabouri Creek" the lot on which the house sits. He also opened a beer garden somewhere nearby in May, 1880, which operated for many years.

He and his wife, the former Clara Schneider, had ten children. One was Mary Wehner, the future Mary Meyer (and later Mary Baumstark) who built the former Meyer Hotel nearby. His descendents still live in the block.

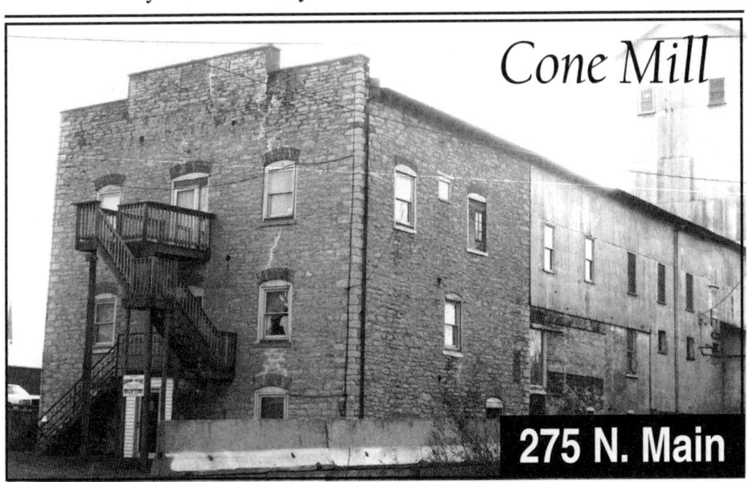

Now housing The Mill Antiques, the former LeCompte Mill was best known as the Cone Mill during the nineteenth century. Believed to have been built in 1856, it was badly damaged in the July, 1880 explosion that killed two men. (See "A Tale of Two Houses.")

The original stone part of the building still retains much of its nineteenth century appearance. The cellar also preserves many early construction details, such as hand-hewn upright supports with chamfered corners and large impost blocks to support the machinery above it, a s well as vertical sawn joists.

The mill was reopened in a matter of weeks in 1880, its façade repaired. A rear brick addition was added early in the twentieth century. The remains of a limestone foundation at the Northeast corner hits that the earlier boiler may have been located there. It was damaged again in 1897 when either a tornado or cyclone ripped through the town, and has struggled to say above flood water in recent decades.

"The survival of much of the original building and the structure's importance in nineteenth century technological development in Ste. Genevieve make this a very important commercial building," the HABS report concluded. This was one of the city's first steam-powered mills.

Leucke, Obermiller Houses 341, 351 N. Main

Determination of the owner saved these attached buildings from the FEMA buyout that followed the 1993 flood. Always at risk due to their location next to the North Gabouri Creek, the connected German vernacular buildings were under several feet of water in 1993 (above, right).

The brick Christian Leucke House (to the South) was built about 1865. The houses have a double entrance, double pile plan and parapet gables. Although the doors are a twentieth century addition, the transoms over both doors appear to be original.

The wooden Wendolin Obermiller House, built about 1850, retains many of its original six-light window sash. The HABS report credits the joined houses with forming "an interesting tableau of mid-nineteenth century houses associated with the town's new German residents."

François Baptiste Vallè House

This grand house – and its owner – barely survived the flood of 1993. Friends and neighbors labored around the clock to keep sandbags ahead of the rising water during the peak of the summer flood. During the ordeal, owner Frank Myers suffered a heart attack. Both house and owner survived.

The circa 1835 Federal double pile house uses ashlar limestone for the front façade and rough fieldstone on the sides to set off the dressed stone on the front. All woodwork in the house is shortleaf pine. The HABS report called it "a handsome and substantial house in a remarkable state of preservation." François Baptiste Vallé, son of Jean Baptiste Vallè, the last Ste. Genevieve commandant, built the impressive house – apparently starting it just after obtaining a large parcel of land from his aging father in 1835. It stands on land once owned by Josiah Millard, who had a house somewhere between this house and the river.

Dendrochronology dates wood in the house to 1832-34, which would have allowed proper seasoning time for construction to have started in 1835. Two other known examples of the cut stone front and fieldstone sides in Ste. Genevieve were the Dufour Stone Building, built about 1818 and the former Church of Ste. Genevieve, built 1832-37.

"A very sophisticated building for its time," according to the HABS report, it was built with a central hallway – a common Federal touch, but rare for early Ste Genevieve. The cellar and attic still include vertical sawn joists, rafters and collar beams. A fireplace opening appears to have been in the cellar – apparently used for cooking and other domestic chores. The house retains much of its original woodwork, including a molded door, window frames and fine Greek Revival mantles.

Built in 1912 as the county poor farm, this fine American Foursquare structure, with a projecting center bay received a large frame addition later. Restored in the 1990s, this long-abandoned building was site of the 1937 hanging of Hurt Hardy — believed to have been the last hanging in Missouri.

Currently Stay'N Play Day Care, it helps extend the historic corridor up North Main Street and Little Rock Road, standing between the Francois Baptiste Valle House and the city park.

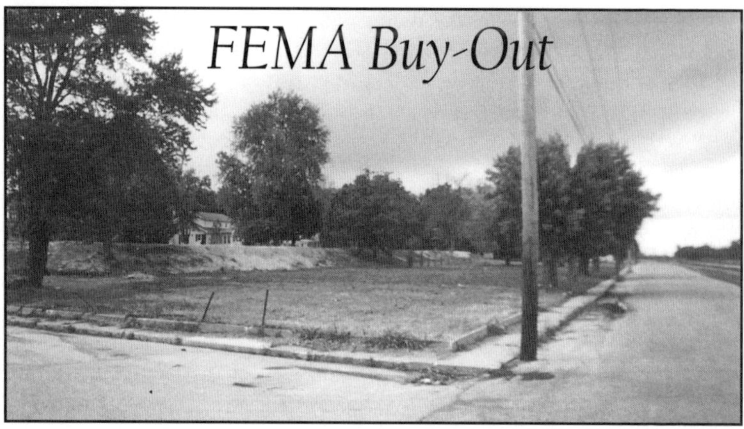

What once was an attractive middle class residential area turned into a hellish landscape of ruins and mud after the 1993 and 1995 floods. It then made the gradual transition to a barren wasteland with just a handful of surviving houses from the North Gabouri to Little Rock Landing, north of town.

The Federal Emergency Management Agency (FEMA) offered owners the chance to take part in a federal buyout and many did so. The homes – some dating into the late nineteenth century – were eventually razed. A few with obdurate owners – or that benefited from strong sandbags in 1993 and 1995 – have survived long enough to see the urban design levee completed in 2000.

Delcommune House

199 LaHaye

Much of the mystery was solved regarding this quaint little house in 2001. Saved from the 1993 flood and partially restored by Ken Kulberg, the structure has a horizontal log first floor – originally believed to be considerably older than the mid-century second floor. Dendrochronology tests, however, returned an 1850 date for those horizontal logs.

The exposed, beaded ceiling joists, puncheon cellar joists and hand-split lath are still visible. Kulberg restored the structure to make the logs visible in the front. This gives the small house a unique and attractive appearance. The frame second story "is also noteworthy," in the words of the HABS report. Two hand-made original doors are still in the upper level. The house is visible from North Main Street/Little Rock Road.

A Tale of Two Buildings

Every neighborhood has its own unique legends, its own unique heritage.

While the northern half of Ste. Genevieve is not perused as often by tourists, the old area contains a fascinating mix of commercial and residential businesses from the nineteenth century. It was here that the influx of German immigrants moved, in large part, in the latter half of the century.

This is the story of two structures on North Main and the relationship between the two.

Standing on the bank of the North Gabouri Creek, The Mill Antique Mall has seen a long and often difficult life. A small limestone portion remains of the original 1856 structure, which was once the commercial hub of the city. Twentieth-century addition greatly enlarge the size of the old mill.

Known as "The Cone Mill," the steam-powered mill was a source of pride to Ste. Genevieve. Advertisements claimed that the mill paid the best prices for grain and turned out the best product in town. By the summer of 1880, the mill had a capacity of 250 barrels of grain in twenty-four hours, which worked out to 40,000 to 50,000 barrels per year. It was managed by a bright young German immigrant, Martin Meyer. Meyer, who had come from Germany to Milwaukee at the age of seven, had just celebrated his seventh wedding anniversary with his young wife, Mary Wehner Meyer, whose father owned a lumberyard

The original section of the old Cone Mill still looks much as it did after its repair following the 1880 explosion.

across the street from the mill. The couple had been blessed with four healthy children since their wedding.

Disaster struck without warning early in the afternoon of July 16, 1880. One of the steam boilers of the Cone Mill exploded in what the *Ste. Genevieve Fair Play* called "the greatest calamity that has ever befallen our city."

An engineer named Koenemann was an immediate fatality, his "lifeless body was found, black and charred, with scarcely a shred of clothing left on it and the whole upper portion of his head blown off," according to the *Fair Play.*

Valentine Seitz, who lived next door to Mary Meyer's father, Nicolas Wehner, was "terribly scalded" and not expected to live. He was taken across the street to be cared for by his wife, Annie, who

The current Main Street Inn was the product of the disastrous Cone Mill explosion.

was expecting their seventh child.

The force of the explosion was fantastic.

"Every building in town was shaken from top to foundation," the *Fair Play* reported. "People thought it was a cyclone."

The engine room was destroyed, the huge chimneys blown hundreds of feet away, into the creek and Nicolas Wehner's beer garden. "Scarcely a brick was left one on another," the newspaper reported. "The whole end of the main building, which was built of stone, is cracked and shattered."

Upon hearing the great explosion, Martin Meyer rushed out of his office and ran outside to see what had happened. He was immediately hit on the head with flying debris.

The loving care of Mary and the best local medical help seemed to be pulling the promising young man back to health. Suddenly a heat wave, complete with the monstrous humidity for which southeast Missouri is famous, struck with fury. In the pre-air condition days, little could be done to keep the invalid cool. Meyer succumbed to the heat and head injuries July 25, nine days after the explosion.

Mary Meyer, two months short of her twenty-sixth birthday, was suddenly a widow with four young children and no income. According to local legend, Mary later collected on a handsome life insurance policy Martin had fortunately held. As grief gave way to a dogged determination to raise her children without leaning on her successful father for support, the widow is said to have invested her insurance money in building the Meyer Hotel.

Whether life insurance money was used is not certain today. Meyer did, however, construct the attractive Second Empire structure (now the Main Street Inn Bed and Breakfast) a few doors down from the mill. This is confirmed in a July 29, 1882 *Ste. Genevieve Herald* story. "Mrs. Mary Meyer is putting up a splendid brick house on the corner of Main and Washington Streets," it read. "It is intended for a hotel."

The Meyer Hotel opened that fall. The next spring an enterprising young man—one year Mary Meyer's junior— named William Baumstartk came to work at the rebuilt Cone Mill. He, like the bulk of Ste. Genevieve's population by then, was a German immigrant.

By 1884 he had married the widow Meyer and was running the Meyer Hotel. Whether it was true love or mutual enlightened financial self-interest that brought the couple together is hard to determine more than a century later. The couple operated the hotel the rest of their lives, though, adding children of their own to those of Mary's first marriage

Seemingly jinxed, the Cone Mill was among the numerous structures hit hard on June 19, 1897, when a fierce windstorm hit the town. Called a tornado by the *Fair Play* and a cyclone by the *Herald*, the storm blew part of the roof, the cupola and both smokestacks off the mill, flattened several barns and blew roofs off a number of houses. It has also struggled to stay above rising flood waters in 1973 and the 1990s. Today it hosts one of the town's largest antique malls.

The old hotel gradually became rundown, but was bought by Ken and Karen Kulberg in the early 1990s. They lovingly restored the Victorian dream of Mary Meyer and the attractive inn has been featured in such national magazines as *Romantic Times.*

Today the home of Valentine Seitz (who carried the scars of his scalding to his death bed almost fifty years, to the day, after the explosion) is owned by his great-grand-daughter. While the last traces of Nicolas Wehner's lumber yard was washed away with the 1973 flood, his home still stands and much of the block is still owned by his descendants.

While the neighborhood is somewhat rundown—many owners were no doubt awaiting the completion of the urban design levee before investing substantially in restoring buildings in the flood plain, it still possesses its late nineteenth-century charm.

The brick storefronts and small houses all have stories to tell of the German families who came from Baden and other points in Germany, to start new lives in Ste. Genevieve. Many are heart wrenching tales of grief and loss; others are uplifting sagas of families defying the odds and finding a way to survive.

The old mill and the former Meyer Hotel have both types of stories to tell.

Off the beaten path ...

Not all of Ste. Genevieve's significant historic buildings are within the official historic district. In fact, many are never seen by visitors at all. This section includes houses either isolated among buildings not as historic, or -- as the title indicates -- so far off the normal downtown itinerary that they are seldom seem.

None of the buildings in this section are generally open to the public.

This deteriorating French Creole cabin was saved from demolition by the Foundation For Restoration of Ste. Genevieve, Inc., and later returned to the Lalumandiere family. Probably built in the first quarter of the nineteenth century, the hard to find little building was called "the most pristine example of a modest Creole house remaining in Ste. Genevieve" by the HABS report.

The HABS authors suggest that the original roof structure is probably intact, with the roof retaining "the typical Creole slant on either side of the ridge." Much of the original material survives intact, including pole rafters that form part of the frame of the porch roof, several puncheoned cellar joists and one unpeeled log sill. The vertical log walls are infilled with rubble noggin. A modern frame addition has been added at the back.

Take Market to Seventh, then follow Seventh across railroad tracks. It becomes South Gabouri. Keep going (past Chadwell Lane) to exit onto Highway 61.

This substantial pre-Civil War home is hidden from most visitors to town as it sits perched on its precipice in the densely wooded area south of Highway 61.

Authors of the HABS report believe the right-hand wing ("perpendicular to the facade") may be older than the rest of the house. Later additions were done in a Greek Revival style, including an imposing porch that rises to the height of the house. A small balcony with wrought iron railing is centered in the "L" of the two wings, on the second floor.

The home of the Donze family for many years, the old house is in an immaculate state of preservation. Turn from Triangle Drive at the intersection of Highways 61 and 32, onto Tenth Street.

Although this book avoids most twentieth century buildings, the tidy row of Craftsman bungalows along Market Street, on the way to Highway 61 cannot pass without mention. These bungalows are significant, if for no other reason, than for their inclusion in the nearly legendary *A Field Guide to American Houses* by Virginia and Lee McAlester.

A bible for architects and students of architecture, preservation and art history, the 1984 book is a required text in university classes across the United States. Naturally the McAlesters included Ste. Genevieve's voluminous French Creole homes in their section on French Colonial architecture. They also picture the row of nine Craftsman homes on Market Street, though, using the bungalows to illustrate various changes and alterations to look for, in identifying house types.

Going out of town on Market, a row of four Craftsman homes appears on the left. After a break, another row of five appears on the same side of the street. All are well maintained and lend a charming and tidy aura to this important entrance and egress to and from the downtown historic district.

Blacksmith's Shop

205 Washington

Built some time after1850, this somewhat dilapidated structure is an important surviving nineteenth century commercial building. The oldest surviving blacksmith's shop in Ste. Genevieve, it seems to maintain much of its original appearance. This includes the mammoth wooden deck across the second story, which draws attention both because of its unique appearance and its apparent deterioration.

The deteriorating I-house next door at 215 Washington has usually been part of the same property. It also dates to around 1850 and has a brick smokehouse in back.

Did you know?

The northern gate to the urban design levee on North Little Rock Road was closed for the first time, June 9, 2001.

Built in 1890, the current Steiger Haus Bed and Breakfast preserves many of its original late nineteenth century details and adds a stately air to the western half of Market Street. The original cast iron fence surrounds the yard, adding to the overall presentation of the house. Behind it, nineteenth century barn has been used to house an outdoor swimming pool for guests. The Steiger Haus, owned by Rob Beckerman, has gained wide renown for its murder mysteries, in which guests are assigned roles and seek clues to the identity of the heinous perpetrator of the crime.

The interior features original boxcar siding, used as ceiling and paneling, as well as door frames with bull's eye motifs in the corners. Square newels with Eastlake jigsaw ornamentation and five-panel doors are also preserved.

Petrequin House/KC Hall

This palatial circa 1910 American Fouresquare/Colonial Revival house is now the home of the local Knights of Columbus chapter. Built by Jules Petrequin, The hemispherical outline of the terraced lawn "mimics the shape of the façade porch and is evidence of an effort to coordinate architecture and landscaping," the HABS report noted.

First School Preschool

145 Washington

Said to have held the first public school in Ste. Genevieve when it was built in 1859, this Anglo-American vernacular brick wall building is most significant for another reason.

It served as the African-American school from 1894 until most blacks left the town in 1930. (See *Ste. Genevieve: A Leisurely Stroll Through History,* "A Dark Night in History," by Bill and Patti Naeger and Mark L. Evans)

The building still has its original six-light window sash and brick dental pattern on the roofline. Restored as a daycare center, the old structure continues to serve in it intended use.

Standing at the corner of Market Street and Highway 61, this mothballed German vernacular house is awaiting an appropriate use. Built around 1860, the brick home is Ste. Genevieve's only example of a double pile, single story, double entrance home – a common German building practice across much of Missouri during the nineteenth century.

A frame addition was added at the rear at a later date. It is owned by a private foundation and is not open to the public.

1399 Market

Augustus Gisi House

Like the Sebastian Butcher House (See page 50), the Joseph Govero House was thought to be entirely heavy timber framed when the HABS teams visited during the 1980s.

Vertical log construction has since been discovered in the oldest portion of the home, however. Built in the first quarter of the nineteenth century, the cellar under the original section still has some large cedar puncheons, used as joists, as well as a hand hewn sill.

Later additions display a variety of stylistic influences in the interior woodwork, including Greek Revival and Italianate.

"The house is well maintained and illustrates a variety of different influences at work in nineteenth century Ste. Genevieve," the report concluded.

Lasource-Durand Cabin

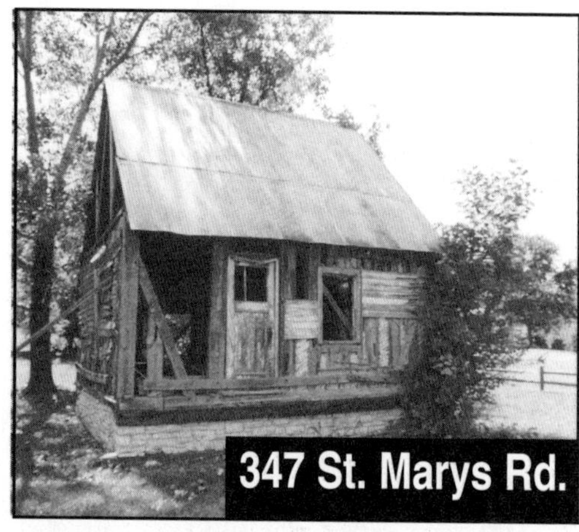

Standing behind the renowned Bequette-Ribault House, the tiny, sagging Lasource-Durand Cabin offers an interesting glimpse into early French Creole building practices. Built about 1807 as the one-room structure seen today, it was expanded to two rooms in 1814 and eventually was enclosed by a five-room house on Chadwell Lane.

In 1983 the modern house was demolished and the original one-room section was dismantled and reassembled at this location. The vertical logs are infilled with *pierrotage*, rather than *bouzillage*, as are the majority of the surviving Creole homes.

Holes in the walls allow the interior walls to be observed, as well. It is privately owned by the Bequette-Ribault owner and is not normally open to the public. The Bequette-Ribault grounds are also private.

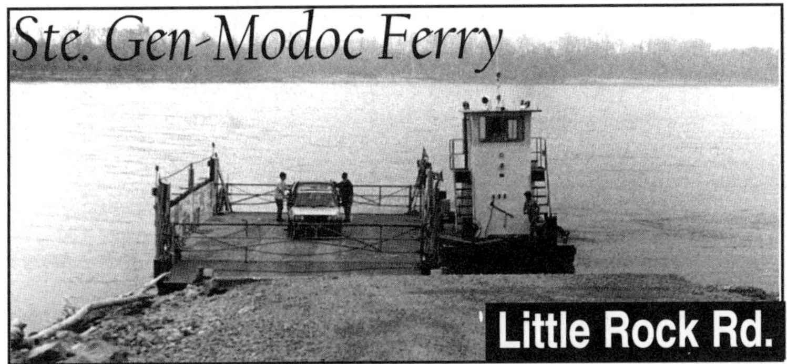

Ferry service is a tradition in Ste. Genevieve that dates back almost as long as the town itself. The service was re-established in the early 1990s, offering motorists quick passage between Ste. Genevieve and historic southeastern Illinois. Modoc and Prairie du Rocher, ILL are both minutes from the Illinois dock.

For a small fee, vehicles and passengers may enjoy the river and get a slight feel of what the keelboat operators and riverboat pilots of bygone days must have experienced, gliding along the river. An even more intimate encounter with the "Father of Waters," the ferry may be reserved for night excursions.

The ferry operates year-round, except during times of extreme water levels or ice. The dock is located at Little Rock Landing, about two miles north of town on Little Rock Road (North Main Street), just past the levee gates and across the railroad track.

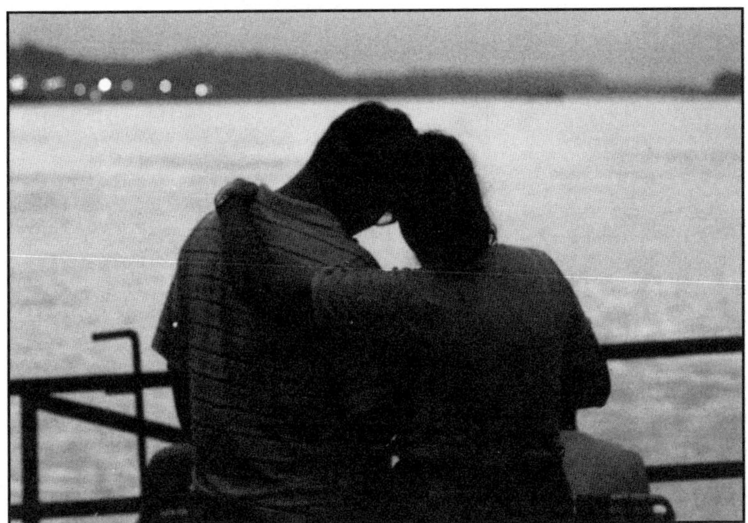

A night ferry excursion offers an escape from the day's troubles.

While Ste. Genevieve is known for its historic treasures that have survived, a sad number of important structures have been lost during the past century.

The town would never have been founded had there not been a vague urging — what we in the twentieth century might call "progress" — prodding Kaskaskia farmers to reach for something a little bit better. Likewise, had the urge to improve their lot not driven the flood-weary colonists up the hill from *le grand champ* in the 1780s and 1790s, no Ste. Genevieve would likely be left today.

That same natural drive to improve one's property and to elevate one's standard of living also led to the continual destruction of old structures and their replacement with newer, more modern buildings.

Historic preservationists philosophize that "You can't save every building." What causes angst in

The aging Misplait House was demolished in 1955.

The attractive Placet-Valle House, probably Ste. Genevieve's last surviving raised Creole cottage, was allowed to burn to the ground in 1936, due to new Ste. Genevieve Fire Department regulations, prohibiting fire calls being made outside the city limits. Possibly built before 1810, it was later the home of Jean Baptiste Valle II.

the Ste. Genevieve saga, though, is that a large number of significant structures from colonial times (and shortly thereafter) still survived at the turn of the twentieth century, only to be lost in the past 100 years.

A few of these losses were significant and the missing buildings are still mourned.

Misplait House

Pierre and Genevieve Misplait (spelling have varied from "Mesplay" to "Mesplait" to "Misplay") were old town residents, who built a fine vertical log home on St. Marys Road in or between 1788 and 1794. The sturdy Creole house was given to their son Basile on his wedding date (to Julie St. Gemme Beauvais), October 2, 1804. The young couple's house served the Misplait family and subsequent owners well.

As the twentieth century wore on, however, age began to take its toll and the old house was not maintained as it might have been. Although it had seen its better days by 1939, Charles E. Peterson, founder of the National Park Department's Historic American Buildings Survey, considered it one of the more important structures in town.

"This interesting little house still shows features characteristic of the early French buildings," he wrote in his *Early Ste. Genevieve and its Architecture*. "The batter of its exterior walls was the familiar local characteristic, the purpose of which has not been explained. In the rear of the house is a stone well with a tent-shaped wooden top and windlass. The form seems to be peculiarly French."

Ste. Genevievians in general had not yet begun to truly appreciate their unique architectural treasures in the mid-1950s. Perhaps it took the splendid restoration of the Bolduc House (completed in 1957) to awaken the town's consciousness. In any case, the Misplait House had reportedly deteriorated to such an extent by the winter of 1955-56 that it was razed.

While no mention can be found in the Ste. Genevieve newspapers at the time, it was loudly bemoaned in the *Missouri Historical Society Bulletin*.

MHS Director Charles van Ravingswaay called the sudden demolition "unexpected and unannounced."

"We regret its passing and deplore the fact that no immediate means could be found to move the fragments from the site and reconstruct the building elsewhere," he wrote in the July 1956 issue.

Even the French well was demolished and filled in. A row of twentieth century houses now runs between the Amoureux and the William Brooks House at the corner of St. Marys Road and Seraphin Street.

Francis Rozier House

Brothers Francis and Felix Rozier each built stately brick mansions on adjoining lots on North Main around 1848. The influential brothers were leading businessmen throughout the nineteenth century.

Dr. Osmund Overby of the University of Missouri believes the Felix Rozier House (now the Inn St. Gemme Beauvais) originally consisted of just the southern half of the

This sketch by Anna Schilli Kirchner is the only known image showing the Felix Rozier House in its entirely.

present building. Built during the Greek Revival period, he feels it may have been a side passage house similar to the Gregoire House on South Fourth.

Mary Rozier Sharp recalled growing up in the Francois Rozier House in her Rozier family biography (with her husband, Louis J. Sharp, III), Between the Gabouri.

"We used most of the eighteen rooms all the time and all of them some of the time," she wrote. "It was a home for cousins' visits, slumber parties, weekends from boarding school, balls, weddings and funerals."

She recalled a vegetable garden behind the house, outlined by boxwood shrubs. A blackberry patch, with fruit trees sat further back from the house. An attractive wrought iron fence on a stone foundation lined the Main Street side of the property, while Sharp recalled a green wooden fence facing Merchant Street.

The Felix Rozier House had the good fortune to pass into the Donze family. The Francis Rozier mansion was not so lucky. Lawrence Donze bought the Felix Rozier House in 1923. Twenty-five years later he passed it on to his son, Norbert Donze. Norbert Donze and his wife Frankye would go on to become probably the most significant local historic restorers in Ste. Genevieve. They converted the stately house into a fine bed and breakfast before if left the family

The Francis Rozier House became one of the last victims of pre-tourism insensitivity to historic architecture. Although the grand old house was still sturdy and attractive, it was deemed less important than downtown parking space. Although space could have been made across the street, before the 1949 construction of the First Baptist Church, or opposite the Felix Rozier, where a car wash would go, the Rozier lot became the virginal sacrifice to progress. The great brick home was torn down in the summer of 1957. The steps from the sidewalk to the front door are still visible on the edge of the parking lot. This was one move many residents wish could be taken back.

Old Church Property

The Church of Ste. Genevieve parish and Valle Catholic Schools held some unusual and historically significant, if decaying, architectural artifacts as the 1950s passed. Sadly, only a fraction of it has survived.

The old convent, originally the Joseph Pratte home, was already standing in1849, when the Sisters of Loretto left the Bolduc-LeMeilleur House and moved into the stately, spacious three-story brick building. They were succeeded by the Sisters of St. Joseph in 1958, who remained in town as long as nuns ran Valle schools. The Valle elementary school, built in 1893, was another huge three-story brick structure, standing just south of the convent.

The modern building program began with the construction of the current Valle High School in 1955. This was a bad omen for the stately old structures on the church and school grounds. The Rev. Joseph E. Ritter, archbishop of St. Louis, seemed to sound the death knell for the historic buildings during his dedication speech at the new high school, December 11, 1955, urging a new convent immediately be built.

"The old building is a fire trap," he told some 1,000 listeners, "and the sisters are too valuable to be placed in such jeopardy in a building that is outmoded and unsafe."

Once again, good intentions led to the loss of valuable pieces of the community's historic fabric. The parishioners proved to be equally unconcerned with preserving the church and community's heritage. The headache ball took the lovely old convent in the fall of 1958, as well as the huge brick grade school.

Even sadder and probably less necessary was the subsequent demolition of the old Joseph Pratte Warehouse which ran along Fourth Street, where the present parish center stands. The charming old limestone structure, built around 1820, was essentially two structures, connected by a rounded center archway. Structures that ran along the outer edge of the owners' property, serving as a fence or stockade as well as a building, seem to have been common in old Ste. Genevieve. Known to twentieth-century parishioners as "The Rock School," the old structure was the last of its kind in Ste. Genevieve. Some have suggested that the structure originally served as the slave quarters for the Pratte property. It was also the first school building in what would later become the Valle schools, serving in that capacity from 1874 until the new elementary building was built in 1893. The stones were supposedly used by local artist Matt Ziegler to build his studio which aligned the Mammy Shaw House

The old convent (left) and the old grade school had a commanding presence until their demolition in the 1950s.

Supposedly built as slave quarters by Joseph Pratte, the circa 1820 Joseph Pratte Warehouse was also the first parochial school in Ste. Genevieve. It was razed in1957 to make way for the new convent -- now the Church of Ste. Genevieve Parish Center.

and the Benjamin Shaw Stone Kitchen for nearly forty years.

Placet-Valle House

One of the more striking houses in the county and one of the nearly-forgotten ones was the Placet-Valle House, which stood atop a high precipice, overlooking Little Rock Landing. Probably built by Michael Placet around 1810 or shortly before.

Photos of the house give the definite appearance of a Creole raised cottage, common in Lower Louisiana and the West Indies, but quite rare for Upper Louisiana. A large stone basement – probably limestone – supported a one and one half story house with a porch or *galerie* running the width of its front. It seemed to bear a strong resemblance to late eighteenth century raised cottages in the current state of Louisiana, such as the Spanish Custom House, Labitut and the Michel Prudhomme House.

The gorgeous old house was later owned by Jean Baptiste Valle (Jr. and Sr.) and was briefly in possession of the famous St. Louis Chouteau family. During the late nineteenth and twentieth centuries, it was in the prosperous Wilder family. Peter Wilder owned much of the Little Rock area and laid out a town grid, hoping to incorporate a separate town of Little Rock. The arrival of the railroad in 1899 was said to put a damper to his plan.

Owned by Andrew Wilder' s widow, the large house was rented as a two-family duplex during the 1930s. A faulty heat stove caused the upstairs to catch fire February 20, 1936. Two years earlier the city of Ste. Genevieve had passed an ordinance banning the city fire department from responding to calls outside the city limits. No rural fire protection existed at the time.

Despite frantic pleas by one of the tenants, the city refused to help and the grand old house burned to the ground. The foundation is still visible, on privately-owned ground. Now the Ste. Genevieve-Modoc Ferry and train tracks are all that are left of Little Rock.

Gregoire House

Although the Judge Peter Huck House (owned by Elmer and Betty Donze) on South Fourth is a jewel in its own right, one of the legitimate French Colonial survivors was sacrificed in 1906, to make way for it.

The circa 1800 home of Charles Gregoire met its fate in 1906.

Charles Gregoire was a major figure in turn of the nineteenth century Ste. Genevieve. His vertical log home appeared to be similar to its next door neighbor, the Guibourd-Valle House and other Creole houses like the Amoureux and Misplait.

Decades before the thought of historic preservation entered the most thoughtful of minds, the old colonial home was demolished, to give Peter Huck, state legislature, circuit judge and prosecuting attorney during a long and distinguished career, the finest home in town.

Old Rottler Building

Historians still argue whether it was Jesse and Frank James and their gang or some other group of desperadoes who robbed the Merchants Bank of Ste. Genevieve on May 26, 1873. Whoever the culprits were, they made off with some $4,000 in loot in the daring broad daylight robbery

The Old Rottler Building, razed in 1934, was supposedly the site of Jesse James bank job in 1873.

and managed to get away without a soul being injured.

Sixty-one years later, in October, 1934, the stately brick building was razed. All that was salvaged was the huge old bank vault that the unknown assailants forced clerk Oliver D. Harris to open, with a gun barrel poked painfully into his temple. The safe is now in the Ste. Genevieve Museum. A modern fire station and tourist rest area now comprise the spot once manned by the Rottler Building. The building was constructed about 1815, supposedly by Jean Baptiste Valle II, and used as a residence until the 1850s, when it became a bank. It was bought by Dr. Louis Guibourd and used as a drug store until 1884, when Charles Rottler purchased it and opened a saloon there. It was said to stand on the site where John James Audubon and Jean Ferdinand Rozier ran their first store, in a vertical log building, in 1811.

Captain St. Gemme House

Built about 1830 by Anthony LeGrave, this gorgeous two-story house just south of town was best known as the home of Gustavus St. Gemme (1844-1912). Known as "Captain" St. Gemme, he was a Civil War veteran and one of Southeast Missouri's most respected historians later in his life. The house, abandoned for a number of years before its destruction in 1973, was known to a later generation of children as "the haunted house," as deterioration began to give its ornate features a decidedly sinister look—especially at night.

Good bye doesn't mean forever

The only eighteenth-century stone house in the immediate Ste. Genevieve area met up with fate in 1991. The historic St. Gemme Stone House, located just outside the city limits on Highway 61, was gradually engulfed by Gegg Excavating. When the current generation of ownership took over

The aging St. Gemme House became known to local youths as "the haunted house."

the company, it was decided that the abandoned house had to go.

To the firm's credit, adequate time was given for the stones to be marked surveyed and carefully disassembled. Owned by a private trust, the components are safely stored, awaiting an appropriate time and place to reassemble the significant 1799 stone house. It is hoped that this will be forthcoming now that the urban design levee has been completed.

The Jean Ferdinand Rozier House was razed in 1880.

One early demolition

One recorded demolition of an early Ste. Genevieve home came in May, 1880, when Henry L. Rozier razed his late father' s home and former storehouse on Merchant Street. "We are glad the old building is being removed as it is in such a delapidated condition that it is fit for nothing," remarked the April 24, 1880 *Ste. Genevieve Fair Play.*

Apparently several older buildings were razed during the early 1880s. Another newspaper article remarked how much better the town looked with some of the old buildings replaced by nice new structures.

The Rozier house seemed to be nearly identical to the Lewis Linn house across the street.

Friday, August 3, 1849

Sampson bit his lower lip as he took the empty buggy back up soggy North Main, toward Little Rock. Without warning, the tears returned. He wiped them away with a weathered right hand. He heard the riverboat's whistle and knew he would arrive just in time.

Just in time to tell Mr. Felix. But *how?* He sighed. *Freedom.* Random thoughts were running piecemeal through his mind – as they had been the past two hours. He would be free. Free to move. Free to work. Free to live. The thought didn't stop the salty tears. It had come so fast. Of course fast was merciful.

Leandre said the commandant had complained of not feeling particularly well when he arose that morning. By mid-morning the diarrhea and the vomiting had started. He had only gotten to see him for moment, the old man squeezing his hand and attempting to smile. He had been gone shortly after noon.

What an end for Mr. Felix's trip. Oh Lord, why do I have to tell him. He sighed deeply as he passed François Baptiste's house. How different it looked today. He wiped his eyes and braced himself. There would be plenty of other important people getting off that boat. He needed to be strong.

Still, as he heard the boat's whistle – today sounding unusually mournful – he found his eyes welling with tears again.

The commandant was dead.

Not everyone agreed with the decision to use the eighty-nine-year-old Jean Baptiste Vallé as the "host" of this book. Trying to depict the one-time commandant interacting with his friends and neighbors as he might have done in the final days of his life in 1849 was a challenge.

If any person could have told Ste. Genevieve's story, though, it would have been J.B. Vallé. He was an adult during both the 1785 and 1844 floods and had had a finger in nearly every major project in between. He was also one of the more learned and cosmopolitan of early Ste. Genevieve residents. Whether he would have been as garrulous as depicted here cannot be known for sure. He was certainly remembered fondly by subsequent generations.

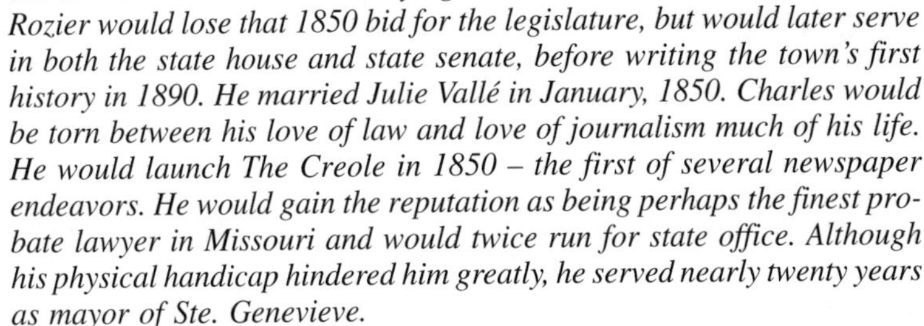

The author squeezed as many important figures who lived in the town in 1849 as possible into the narrative. The pregnant Augustine Menard (who would have seven children) would go on to be considered the town's most noted historian in her old age – as would her brother, Captain Gustavus St. Gemme.

Jean Ferdinand Rozier would live to be nearly as old as the old commandant, dying in 1864. Firmin Rozier would lose that 1850 bid for the legislature, but would later serve in both the state house and state senate, before writing the town's first history in 1890. He married Julie Vallé in January, 1850. Charles would be torn between his love of law and love of journalism much of his life. He would launch The Creole in 1850 – the first of several newspaper endeavors. He would gain the reputation as being perhaps the finest probate lawyer in Missouri and would twice run for state office. Although his physical handicap hindered him greatly, he served nearly twenty years as mayor of Ste. Genevieve.

Mid-way through the writing, the author discovered an 1850 letter, in which Lucy Desloge – a cousin to both the Vallés and Roziers – stated that the old commandant had died of cholera during a local epidemic. The St. Louis Republican confirmed that St. Louis was being inundated with the disease during the days prior to his death. This information was added to the narrative. It is hoped that the commandant's death was indeed as speedy as depicted here. Late in the writing, meanwhile, Jim Baker, site director of the Felix Vallé State Historic Site, provided the names and ages of Vallé's slaves. Among them were a fifty-two-year-old named Sampson and a twenty-six-year-old named Leandre.

Mark L. Evans
June 8, 2001

Notes on building selections

Choosing which buildings to include in this work and which ones to exclude was a somewhat daunting task. Early in the project I drove myself crazy. Every time I would see an 1890s building I wanted to include, I reminded myself of all the circa 1850 buildings I *wasn't* planning on including. "How can I put this one in, if I don't have all those in?" I kept asking myself.

I finally reached a decision. In essence, I wound up telling my conscience to shut up. I finally decided that I was the author or the *artiste* and that it was *my* book. To use the somewhat crude vernacular, I would choose the buildings that "floated my boat" and let others worry about how the decisions were made. Once I reached that stage, the task became much easier.

Most architects, historians or anyone else with much background on Ste. Genevieve would probably have little trouble agreeing on the twenty or thirty most important buildings in town. Beyond that, though, it becomes quite subjective. No doubt many will be shocked that I did not include every single French Creole structure in town. After all, Ste. Genevieve's greatest claim to significance is possessing more of these than any other city in North America. Generally, though, I shied away from houses whose primary significance was a vertical log room or two, buried deep within a much later house. One exception was the François Vallé II House, whose association with Vallé — not to mention its small uncovered section of vertical logs on the front — make it very significant, despite its late nineteenth century appearance.

I tried to have a wide variety of styles. The newest building included is the Ste. Genevieve Junior High. Built as the high school as a 1936 WPA project, it stands on its own merit. Plus, a sixty-five-year-old school building is roughly equal to a 150-year-old home. Otherwise, I mention little from the recent century. I do hit many more commercial buildings than anyone has dealt with in the past. The Victorian era solidity and charm of the brick and pressed metal storefronts lends Ste. Genevieve an extra layer of charm that few consciously appreciate. A 200-year-old wall of *poteaux en terre,* with *bouzillage* or *pierrotage* between the posts is certainly awe-inspiring; so, too, though, is an original, ornate pressed metal store front of the Gilded Age (like Myers Shoes) or the gorgeous combination of a bright shutter contrasting against ashlar limestone.

Yes, there are a few buildings I feel a bit remiss about leaving out. I'm sure many who know Ste. Genevieve architecture will be surprised to see the Louis and Joseph Caron Houses on Roberts Street and a few other French Creole buildings omitted. I also felt guilty in a few instances, choosing the majority of, but not all, buildings in a block. I almost included the

Anthony LaGrave Building at 58 South Main and Otte's Cleaners at 39 North Main. Yet I felt I had more than enough brick commercial vernacular buildings included. Likewise, not every German vernacular brick structure made it, either. A few, like the Charles Jokerst House in North Fourth, the Augustus Wilder Building on the square, the Martin Intress House on North Third and the two fine German brick farm houses just out of town on Highway M, possibly should have been included. A good argument can be made for the Greek Revival Augustus Bequette House on North Second.

LaGrave Building

In fact, good arguments are welcome. It is my hope that this book may enjoy enough success to see at least one more edition printed. Any building owners who believe their house should have been included – or who feel the information printed on their building here was wrong – are encouraged to contact me at 1025 W. Cape Rock Drive; Cape Girardeau, MO 63701 or at mlevans@brick.net. If someone can convince me that a change should be made, I will be happy to make it, should any subsequent editions be printed. Otherwise, I hope the selection proves interesting and informative to its readers.

Otte's Cleaners

Mark L. Evans
June 8, 2001

BIBLIOGRAPHY

Brackenridge, Henry Marie, *Recollections of the Persons and Places in the West,* Philadelphia: J.B. Lippincott & Co., 1868.

Connally, Ernest Allen, "Restoration of the Bolduc House at Sainte Genevieve," 1958.

Desloge, Lucy to unknown relative, July 28, 1850, Missouri Historical Society.

Ekberg, Carl J., *Colonial Ste. Genevieve,* Tucson: The Patrice Press, 1996

Franzwa, Gregory M., *The Story of Old Ste. Genevieve,* St. Louis: The Patrice Press, 1990.

Guibourd, Omar, diary, *Missouri Historical Society Bulletin Vol. VIII*: St. Louis, 1952.

Guyette, Richard P., *Tree Ring Dating of French Colonial Vertical Log Houses in Ste. Genevieve, Missouri,* Columbia: the University of Missouri-Columbia, 1985.

__________________, *Wood Use in French Colonial Vertical Log Houses in Ste. Genevieve, Missouri,* Columbia: the University of Missouri-Columbia, 1985.

Guyette, Richard P. and Overby, Osmund, "The first tree ring dating of a building in Missouri," *Missouri Preservation News,* Fall, 1984.

History of Southeast Missouri, Chicago: The Goodspeed Publishing Co., 1888.

Naeger, Bill and Patti, with Evans, Mark L., *Ste. Genevieve: A Leisurely Stroll Through History*, Ste. Genevieve: Merchant Street Publishing, 1999.

Overby, Osmund, Historic *American Buildings Survey,* HABS No. MO-1109, Columbia: 1987

__________________, *Ste. Genevieve Architectural Survey,* Columbia: University of Missouri-Columbia, 1985.

Peterson, Charles E. "A Guide to Ste. Genevieve, with Notes on its Architecture," National Park Service, 1939.

Petrequin, Harry J., *Stories of Old Ste. Genevieve:* Cape Girardeau, 1934.

Scharp, Mary Rozier and Sharp, Louis J., III, *Between the Gabouri*. Ste. Genevieve: Histoire de Rozier, 1981.

Ste. Genevieve *Fair Play*, various issues.

Ste. Genevieve *Herald*, various issues.

Personal Communication

Jim Baker, 1997, 1998, 2001

Fran Ballinger, 1997

Lucille Basler, 1997, 1998

Timothy G. Conley, 1996, 1997, 2001

Ernest Allen Connally, 1997
Carl J. Ekberg, 1996, 1997, 1998, 2001
Gregory M. Franzwa, 1997, 1998
Hilliard J. Goldman, 2001
Richard P. Guyette, 1997, 2001
Michael Hankins, 2001
Jack Luer, 1997
Osmund Overby, 1997, 1998, 2001
Charles E. Peterson, 1997, 1998

PHOTO CREDITS

The author gratefully acknowledges photographs in this book that were used with permission from the following soucres. Only the page number is listed if that photo is the only one that page.

Janet Abt Collection
65, 130 (Misplait House), 135, 136, 139 (Rozier House)
Fran Ballinger Collection
5 (ribbon cutting), 8 (Connally honored), 10
Timothy G. Conley Collection
94 (Academy before restoration)
Hoffman Family Collection
53
Missouri Historical Society
15, 70, 138, 139 (St. Gemme House)
Bill Naeger Collection
9 (Bolduc-LeMeilleur as hotel), 17 (Charles H. Biel store), 116 (Leucke, Obermiller Houses during flood), 131 (Placet-Valle House, top photo), 137
State Historical Society of Missouri
7 (Charles E. Peterson photo, 1941)

All other photos were taken by the author. Some had appeared in the *Ste. Genevieve Herald* between 1996 and 1999.

ART CREDITS

Front cover art is by Janet Kraus. The closeup of the commandant on the rear cover and several interior pages is from a 1938 Bernard Peters painting located in the Guibourd-Valle House.

Anna Schilli Kirchner pen and ink sketches appear on pages 24, 88, 107 and 137.

Mark L. Evans is a freelance writer living in Cape Girardeau, MO, where he is pursuing his master' s degree in history at Southeast Missouri State University. A journalist for sixteen years, he has worked at newspapers in Dexter, Kennett, Farmington, Poplar Bluff, Cape Girardeau and Ste. Genevieve, MO. He has won ten Missouri Press Association "Better Newspaper Contest" awards and two Missouri Associated Press Managing Editors awards.

A Bonne Terre, MO native, he received a BA in history from Central Methodist College in Fayette, MO in 1985 and contributed to *Central Methodist College: 1961-1985,* edited by Dr. Bartlett C. Jones in 1986. He also contributed chapters to *The Lure and Lore of Missouri Basketball*, edited by George Sherman, in 1992. In 1999 he and Bill and Patti Naeger co-authored *Ste. Genevieve: A Leisurely Stroll Through History.* He is also working on a book on the history of Old St. Vincent's Church in Cape Girardeau and has been chosen to author a Missouri Alliance For Historic Preservation book on historic preservation in the state.

Evans is single and enjoys reading, watching movies, barefoot hiking, visiting historical sites and playing APBA baseball and on-line trivia.

Janet Kraus is an artist whose heart if not her home is grounded in Ste. Genevieve. Since joining the Ste. Genevieve Art Guild in the early 1990s, she has captured the homes and gardens of the city in water colors. Her largest work is a large mural based on the town as it might have appeared about 1850. It is displayed in the Old Louisiana Academy. She is also a member of the Jefferson County Art Guild and was chosen "Artist of the Year 2000" by that group.

Kraus is a resident of Imperial, MO and resides there with her husband. They have four children and nine grandchildren.

Anna Schilli Kirchner adds a breath of fresh country air to her realistic style of art work. Living and working in the scenic and historic Ste. Genevieve County, MO area furnishes her with endless subject matter for her works. Accomplished in oils, watercolor, pen and ink, and sculpture Kirchner has been accepted into juried shows and has received top honors. Her works are in corporate and private collections worldwide.

She is a member of the St. Louis Watercolor Society, Arts Council of Southeast Missouri and president of the Ste. Genevieve Art Guild.

The following sponsors helped make this book possible

Law Office of

Rottler & Huelskamp

A Professional Corporation

Ste. Genevieve, Mo.

1-800-670-5793

Terry R. Rottler, Attorney At Law   Robert Huelskamp, Attorney At Law

- Signature Sculpture & Wood Works
- Ste. Genevieve County Memorial Hospital
- Joseph W. Sharlow, M.D.
- Sara's Ice Cream & Antiques

In memory of Frankye and Norbert Donze, Ste. Genevieve's pioneer preservationists and original restorers of

Inn St. Gemme Beauvais
Vital St. Gemme Beauvais House
Green Tree Inn
Amoureux House
Dr. Charles Hertich House

Pick up a copy of the book everyone is talking about:

Ste. Genevieve: A Leisurely Stroll Through History **available at Bill's Photo Lab, 123 Merchant St. (573) 883-3221**

A wonderful gift any time of year!

Ste. Genevieve Herald

Ste. Genevieve County's News Source For 120 Years

P.O. Box 447
Ste. Genevieve, MO 63670
573-883-2222.

In Memoriam

Valle Weber Fay

Born St. Louis, Mo., March 5, 1919
Died Norwalk, Ct., January 22, 1997

The great-great-great granddaughter of Francois Valle II, who took the appreciation for the preservation of historical architecture from Ste. Genevieve to her adopted hometown in Connecticut where she led the lengthy fight to preserve the 19th Century commercial buildings of South Norwalk that today make up the nationally honored SoNo Historic District.

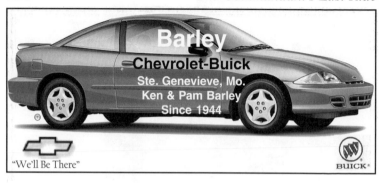

HOLNAM